YO-ARS-323

THE YEARS FROM ONE TO SIX

CHILD AND MATERNAL HEALTH DIVISION

FIRST EDITION 1950
MAJOR REVISION 1971

Published by authority of
the Honourable John Munro
Minister of National Health and Welfare

Maurice LeClair, M.D.
Deputy Minister of National Health

Joseph W. Willard
Deputy Minister of National Welfare

© Crown Copyrights reserved

Available by mail from Information Canada, Ottawa
and at the following Information Canada bookshops:

HALIFAX
1735 Barrington Street

MONTREAL
Æterna-Vie Building, 1182 St. Catherine Street West

OTTAWA
171 Slater Street

TORONTO
221 Yonge Street

WINNIPEG
Mall Centre Building, 499 Portage Avenue

VANCOUVER
657 Granville Street

or through your bookseller

Price $1.00   Catalogue No. H53-170

Price subject to change without notice

Information Canada,
Ottawa 1971

Foreword

"Up The Years From One To Six" follows the book "The Canadian Mother and Child". It has been written primarily for mothers and fathers, but also for students, professional educators, and all who are concerned in the promotion of total health of young girls and boys.

The years between one and six are years of rapid development. It is during this five year period that parents and their children strengthen their bonds of love and security. This is the time young children build the foundation of their future health, the period when they learn to relate to other human beings. The groundwork for knowing oneself and respecting the rights and responsibilities of others is laid in these early years.

It is being stressed constantly that children from birth on must be considered as human beings, possessing physical, mental, social, emotional and spiritual capabilities; knowledge of them as unique personalities with specific needs has increased considerably in the last decades. It is sincerely hoped that this book will bring new information and understanding of children to those who read it, and with this realization, contribute to the good health and well-being of Canadian children. The final objective is persons who will know who they are, who will care for and about themselves and others.

Although reference is made to the young child as HE, readers should, of course, interpret the subject matter to relate to girls as well as boys.

Acknowledgements

In revising this book, the Child and Maternal Health Division greatly appreciates the assistance received from many medical and health authorities across Canada. Technical reviews were made by the Maternal and Child Health Advisory Committee of the Department of National Health and Welfare, the Canadian Peadiatric Society, and provincial medical and nursing consultants in maternal and child health.

Consultants in the Divisions of Dental Health, Epidemiology, Mental Health, and Nutrition of the Department of National Health and Welfare acted as advisers in their specific areas of concern.

The excellent cooperation extended to the division has made possible the revision of "Up The Years From One To Six" in its present form.

Cover design: Child's art by permission of the Ottawa Board of Education.

Your Child

Your child is now one year old. During the next five years, it will be your privilege to share and enjoy with your child the fascinating process of growth and development to the full.

The love established earlier should be strengthened in these first early years and become the basis of many of

your child's most important life experiences. You will be continually learning about your child by observing the way he acts, communicates and plays. By understanding how different children can be, you will be able to avoid many of the problems that are created by parents who try to press their child into one mold.

At any moment, your child reflects a mixture of all his past experiences, his present absorption in whatever he is doing and hints of what is to come. No two children are alike. Each child is a unique individual unlike his brother or sister or friend across the street. How your child grows and develops physically, mentally, socially and emotionally depends on many factors including when and where he was born, the order of his birth in relation to other members of the family, the number of other children in the family, and various family traits. It can be observed that some children are thin or chubby, others shy or loud. A number grow rapidly while others grow more slowly. Differences are normal and expected in healthy children.

While every child is unique, there is a range of predictable patterns that are common to all children. However, few children will fit these patterns at every stage of their development. Striking changes take place in the size and shape of the different parts of each child's body. The first year of life is the period of most rapid growth. Children usually triple their birth weight and increase about eight inches in height by their first birthday. During the second year, the increase in weight and height is about half of that in the first year. After the third year, the expected annual weight gain is about four pounds, and the expected increase in height is about two inches a year up to puberty.

It may also help to know that some annoying behaviour of a child is part of what all children go through. A one-year-old can drink from a cup, creep and crawl rapidly, contribute a few words to the conversation such as

"Mama" and "Dada", and distinguish members of his family from strangers. He plays enthusiastically and participates with delight in each step of the daily routine. He is beginning to have his own ideas about what he wants to do, where he wants to go, what he wants to eat, how he feels about strangers and many other things. This shows that a child is growing up.

Between two and three years of age, a child usually has learned enough words to make himself understood concerning his surroundings, his needs, likes and dislikes. He speaks in sentences, begins to appreciate time, colours, and other differences in his environment. He becomes more and more competent with his hands. From crude beginnings, placing one block on another, then building a "bridge" with three blocks, he develops a sense of form and simple numbers.

A child of three is imitative, constructive, destructive, alert and noisy — never still for a moment. Such activity should not be considered as a sign of "nervousness". It is natural. There are many things which a three-year-old can do without help, such as feeding, washing his hands and some dressing and undressing. It will be found that he is much better at undoing, untying and taking off than he is at doing, tying and putting on. His curiosity will urge him to keep trying things and he should be encouraged as much as possible.

A four-year-old is more capable still with his hands. He can now draw simple figures of objects, people, and animals. His sense of form and rhythm are becoming more evident. He can button, unbutton, and untie, although he does not succeed very well at tying. He can tell stories, recount events, repeat simple nursery rhymes. He begins to show a tendency towards highly imaginative play, and is very curious and quick to learn. He plays with a few other children.

From five to six years, a child's development proceeds rapidly. He is more accurate in the use of his hands, he can draw with fair accuracy, and he mixes easily in a group of children his age. He should now be able to dress and undress completely, but may need help in tying knots.

This book does not pretend to describe young children as interesting or as engaging as they really are, nor does it mean to portray them as neat little packages. No rigid set of rules can be given for bringing up children. For quick reference and for emphasis, a number of aspects of child care have been separated out and described briefly. It is left to the readers to apply the information to their own particular circumstances, as they help the individual child in his process of growing up.

Table of Contents

PART I

GROWTH AND DEVELOPMENT

PART II

BEHAVIOUR

PART III

POTENTIAL BEHAVIOUR PROBLEMS

PART IV

THE HANDICAPPED CHILD

PART V

THE SICK CHILD

PART I

Growth & Development

CHAPTER 1

Daily Routine

Regardless of the changes in our style of family living, parents are directly responsible for the care, protection and health promotion of their children. This means attending to a child's needs every day to help him to form good health habits and to develop into a healthy personality.

Health promotion is a big job and one that cannot be carried out exactly the same way for all children. No child inherits the habits of a well regulated daily health routine; they must be formed.

Some of the guidelines suggested for parents in leading their children in the direction of good health are:

1. Keep the home in which the young child lives a loving and trusting one.

2. Provide a child with the necessary foods and help him in the formation of good food habits.

3. Guide and encourage him in good health and social practices by care and good example.

4. Protect him from accidents and injuries by practising and teaching everyday safety.

5. Protect him from contagious diseases by having him immunized.

6. Provide for regular medical and dental visits.

7. Attend to his special needs when he is sick.

Although a number of the major health subjects will be described in separate chapters, for example, nutrition, dental health and safety, and others will appear elsewhere in the book, comments on some matters affecting the health of the young child are presented at this time.

Sleep

Sleep is nature's great restorer. An adequate period of restful sleep is necessary for your child's physical and mental health. Since young children usually awake early in the morning they should be put to bed early in the evening to ensure an adequate amount of rest. Young children need about twelve hours of sleep a day. It is often wise to maintain the daily afternoon rest until your child is five years old.

Children are normally restless sleepers some of the time and sound sleepers other times. If your child has prolonged or repeated periods of wakefulness, disturbed sleep or restlessness accompanied by frightening dreams, something is wrong and should be corrected. After he has gone to bed for the night, do not pick him up immediately just because he cries or asks for something. Satisfy yourself that there is no physical cause for discomfort, then leave him for a while. There is, however, little point in letting him work himself into a state of excitement when a little attention and affection would reassure him and permit him to settle down. If his failure to go to sleep persists, this might indicate some temporary stress. Putting a child back in bed when he is still restless and sobbing could result in such bedtime behaviour as refusing to go to bed without a light, or without a parent lying down by his side. Some children who are excitable and overactive often suffer from sleep disturbances — their minds are still busy with thoughts of the day's activities. For such a child, an afternoon rest which cuts down the amount of his physical and mental activities and a quiet time before bed often results in better sleep at night. An exhausted child does not necessarily sleep well.

Clothing

A child's clothes, whether bought or made, should meet the five following requirements:

1. Clothing should fit easily so that he can move about freely.

Since a young child is learning to make all kinds of movements, his clothes should not hinder him in any way. You should make sure there are no tight bands around his arms, knees, waist or between his legs.

2. Clothing should be of suitable weight so that a child is neither too hot nor too cold.

Your child should wear only enough clothes to keep him comfortable. The amount of clothing necessary will vary with the child as well as with the temperature. Many mothers make the mistake of clothing their youngsters too warmly. You can check on your child's comfort by slipping your hand under his clothes down along the skin of his back. If he feels moist, he is too warm and the amount of his clothing should be reduced. Plastic (rubber) pants are very useful, but do not leave them on a wet child because they will hold the moisture in and cause irritation.

3. Clothing should be washable, soft and comfortable.

You can expect your youngster to get dirty, therefore you should use easily washable materials, preferably not too light in colour. They should be able to stand plenty of hard wear, but they should be soft so that his skin will not be chafed. Do not use strong detergents or bleaches for laundry as they may cause skin rashes. Be sure to rinse all the clothes well. Clothes that are knitted or made out of man-made fibers, seersucker, corduroy or jersey need little or no ironing and will save a lot of time and work. Two-piece sleepers, flannelette or terrycloth, with feet, are good for night wear. They are easy to detach for changing and washing when your child is learning to keep dry.

4. Clothing should be safe.

Your child's clothes should be free from ornaments such as buckles, loose buttons, or beads which are in any way dangerous. Care should be taken that the materials of his clothes are "non-flammable". In some cases the clothes are marked in this way.

5. Clothing should be simple, so that he can learn to dress and undress himself.

The time at which he learns to dress himself depends on the child himself, the help you give him and the type of clothes you provide. If your child's clothes are simple with wide openings and large buttons and buttonholes in the front, he will learn how to manage them easily. Pants that have elastic are the easiest to pull up and down and will assist him in going to the toilet himself, when he is around three.

Children primarily wear shoes for protection from injury and cold; it is not harmful to walk barefoot in safe surroundings. When buying shoes make sure they are well made, give good support, and have adequate room for the toes. Pointed-toed shoes do not fit young children's feet. Shoes should be fitted on a child and they may have to be replaced often, as the feet grow. Do not pass a child's outgrown shoes on to other children unless you are sure they fit correctly. If his feet are sore, red or irritated, consult the doctor.

Stockings or socks that are too short often cramp the feet. Buy your child's socks about a half inch longer than his feet. Cotton socks are generally best.

Care In The Sun

It is good for a child to be in the sun for a period of the day, but be careful to increase gradually the periods when he is in the direct sun because his skin may be very sensitive. It is best for a child to wear light clothing that does not expose too much skin to the sun. When the weather is hot, he should wear a thin cotton hat.

Posture

Good posture is the natural balance and poise of the body in all positions: standing, sitting, lying and in action. Proper foods, sleep and rest, well fitting shoes and socks, fresh air and play, and confidence from a loving happy home atmosphere, all play a part in the development and maintenance of good posture. By six years of age, feet should point straight ahead, and knees should be straight. Balance and coordination will develop as your child grows and uses his muscles. Parents should encourage good posture and when necessary, correct poor posture.

Activities and Rest

Young children need plenty of activity such as creeping, crawling, sliding, climbing and walking for physical and mental stimulation.

The basement or backyard should afford ample space for running, jumping and climbing. Many things will help develop your child's muscles and teach him balance and poise. Pedal toys such as a tricycle strengthen the leg and feet muscles. Bars or ladders give a child lots of opportunity for large muscle activity.

The amount of a child's activity has to be watched since he does not always know when to rest. If your child is overactive he is liable to become cross, tired and lose his appetite. You can help him by cutting down on the amount of his activity. On the other hand, children who do not get enough activity tend to be irritable and generally bad humoured. This can be overcome if you promote more activity for this type of child.

Play

"To play is to live." Children need to play to develop their muscles and enjoy physical activities. Play stimulates their minds and bodies. It is desirable to have both a safe indoor and outdoor space where your child can play. Playing in fresh air is always best. Some play out of doors in both winter and summer is recommended. In winter, close supervision is necessary to make sure your child is comfortable and does not stay out too long in extreme cold. If he does not move about he may become intensely cold without realizing it.

A child will benefit if he has the opportunity of playing with a few other children his age in a safe, open place, under kindly supervision. This will help him develop habits of good comradeship with his playmates. Playground areas where children can usually use public equipment under qualified supervision are a valuable asset in any community.

As your child grows up he should be given toys appropriate for his age. Select toys carefully, avoiding those that are pointed, sharp or otherwise dangerous. Fragile toys should not be selected since splintered parts or rough, jagged edges of broken pieces can lead to injury. Toys do not have to be elaborate or expensive. Toys are used to enrich play, provide enjoyment, and teach responsibility.

Your child will enjoy playing in a sandbox with a pail and shovel. This will give him an opportunity to be creative with physical materials.

Toilet Habits

There is no advantage in trying to train your child to be dry before he is old enough to understand what he is doing. Children's bowel movements usually occur at the same hour each day, but a few children do not have a daily bowel movement. There are variations and you will know your child's bowel timing from observation. By about two years he generally will be able to ask to go to the toilet during the day. By the age of three he will usually keep his clothes and bed dry. You can help him attain the dry habit by observing when he usually goes and by taking him to the toilet at those times, for example, either before or after each meal, before or after his sleep, before he goes to bed, and before or after going outside. In difficult cases, avoid giving him liquids in large quantities after four o'clock in the afternoon and do not permit him to exercise actively after supper.

Cleanliness

Children are not naturally clean in their habits. They have to learn through those of their parents. Good habits of cleanliness in parents are quickly noted and imitated. You will want him to make a habit of washing his hands with soap and water after he uses the toilet and before he eats.

It may not be necessary to give your child a daily bath, especially in winter, but when he is dirty he should have one. If he is imitating you, by two he will enjoy learning to wash himself. Help him until he can do it on his own. You might keep a small bench or stool handy to help him reach the sink and taps. However, watch him constantly so that he does not burn himself with hot water.

Wash your child's hair once a week, taking care to dry his head completely, especially during winter. The eyes, ears and nose do not call for special care and he should not attempt to clean the inside of his ears or nose.

The water should feel comfortable to the touch of your elbow. Supervise the bath carefully since there is a danger of accidents from falls, burns from hot tap water, and drowning in even a small amount of water. Teach your child to view bathtime as one of the most pleasant periods of the day. Encourage him to wash and dry himself and praise him when he does it well. If possible, your child should have his own towel for daily use.

Your child should learn to keep his clothes reasonably clean and in good condition. However, do not be strict to the point of preventing him from frisking about, simply because he may dirty or tear his clothes. If necessary, change all his clothes after playtime. This habit will teach him the importance attached to cleanliness and the care of clothing.

Television

Because of the attraction of sound, light and movement, television has a great appeal for young children. When they are very young, children stay near the TV set but will go off to play with toys from time to time; but it is well known that some children are content to look at television many hours. Television is probably here to stay, and parents have found it has good points and, of course, some not so good. In addition to its truly educational value, it has an entertainment value hard to equal. Parents will have to consider what they feel is important for a child to see and do; television should not be allowed to take up all a child's time and interest; other activities should be provided. Instead of complaining about television programs undesirable for children, parents might try to see that better programs are presented.

CHAPTER 2

Health Supervision

In addition to the day to day care given a child at home, he should receive regular attention from others, namely doctors, dentists, nurses, and teachers. This is needed in order to promote a child's total health, his physical, mental and social well-being. No longer is a person considered healthy just because he is not suffering from an illness. With the emphasis on prevention and promotion, a healthy child is one who enjoys good physical health, who feels happy and secure in his parent's love, and who enjoys playing, eating, and sleeping.

More and more it is being appreciated that parents need help in promoting their child's total health. Most municipalities provide free clinics where children can be protected against the more serious communicable diseases by immunization. Well child conferences provide both counselling and immunization services for the pre-school child. Family allowances paid monthly for each child by the federal government afford financial assistance to parents in providing their children with some care and security. The allowances may be used toward supplying an increased amount of nourishing food, a periodical dental or medical examination, warm clothing, or in any other of a variety of useful ways. It would be worthwhile to find out the kind of assistance in matters of health available in your community.

Every child should be taken regularly to a public health clinic or to his own physician. Doctors, dentists, nurses and other health workers can help you with your child's health promotion in the following ways:

1. by periodic health appraisals (physical examination)
2. by immunization against certain communicable diseases
3. by screening tests
4. by consultations between you and other people interested and involved with children, such as kindergarten and school teachers.

Periodic Health Appraisals

As stated in the "Canadian Mother and Child," every baby should be carefully examined by a doctor shortly after birth. At that time you, as parents, would have been advised about the care your child requires. In general, every child should be seen by a physician and/or nurse about six or more times in the first year of life. A child is usually seen two or more times in the second year, and about one or more times yearly thereafter. Children who have been sick or have some form of handicap, however, may require closer supervision.

The purpose of these visits is to enable you, your child, and the doctor or nurse to meet and to discuss the child's growth and development since his last visit, to assess his emotional, physical and social development and to plan what should be done to help him in the future. Thus the doctor's physical examination is only one part of the visit. Occasionally a doctor may refer a child and his parents to other health workers for further examinations or advice. Consultation with a psychologist, or a psychiatrist, or a child guidance clinic worker can often help parents and children to deal with particular behaviour problems.

Young children are usually first taken to a dentist between the ages of two and one-half and three. (See Chapter 4.)

Immunization

Immunization is the name given to the means by which the body is stimulated to develop protection against certain diseases. At different times in various countries, different diseases are prevalent, but with immunization children can be protected for a long period of time from many of these diseases. In the future, protection will likely become available against even more diseases.

Presently, it is recommended by health departments that all healthy children in Canada be immunized against the following diseases: diphtheria, pertussis, tetanus, poliomyelitis, measles, and smallpox. No doubt your child has already received some of these immunizations, as it is important that protection be given early in life. It would be well to check his immunization records at this time.

Immunization against *Diphtheria, Pertussis* (whooping cough) and *Tetanus* (lockjaw), often referred to as DPT is given by injection. The vaccine is given in three doses at one to two month intervals, usually starting after three months of age. The protection is maintained by reinforcing or booster injections given at one and one-half to two years of age and again at intervals recommended by your doctor or health department. There is reason to believe that these boosters will be necessary less often than previously recommended.

The immunization against *Poliomyelitis* can be given in two different ways. The vaccine may be combined in the same injection with the diphtheria, pertussis and tetanus mentioned above, or it may be given in a live virus form by mouth, giving a more complete and permanent protection. The live virus doses are given during infancy and are repeated later. The live virus is often given to infants or to older children who have already started their poliomyelitis immunization by injection.

The immunization against *Measles* is generally carried out by injection of live virus vaccine. It is best given after 12 months of age. In some places, infants may receive initial immunization by killed measles vaccine combined with the diphtheria, pertussis, whooping cough, and polio vaccine. However, the live measles injection must be given in addition to this.

Smallpox Vaccination is best done during the second year of life. For international travel a vaccination is valid for only three years. Vaccination should not be performed on a child with eczema, or where someone with this disease could come in contact with the newly vaccinated child.

The live virus vaccine for *German Measles* (rubella) is new. It may be administered to all children over the age of one, but public health programs will probably immunize certain age groups first. German measles is a mild disease in children, but a serious one in adults, especially for a pregnant woman. In this case, the disease may cause damage to her unborn baby.

Live virus vaccine for *Mumps* may be used in children over the age of one. Because of the mildness of this disease, immunization is not always considered important.

The following additional immunizations may be recommended by the doctor for certain children.

When children are boating in polluted water, or are travelling to areas where typhoid is prevalent, they may be given some protection against *Typhoid* and *Paratyphoid* fever by a series of two to three injections. This vaccine requires reinforcing doses given later on.

Immunization against *Cholera* and *Yellow Fever* are compulsory or recommended for those travelling to some areas of the world. Your physician or health department can supply information on this matter.

Vaccines against *Influenza* are usually used in cases where there is an increased risk of complications, for example, a child with congenital heart disease. The vaccines are only good against specific influenza virus types, e.g. Asiatic influenza.

At the present time vaccines against the *Common Cold* are not generally recommended.

If children are exposed to conditions listed below, they may be helped to avoid the disease or escape complication, if a doctor is consulted early.

Diseases or Conditions	Substances a Physician May Prescribe for Prevention
Bee stings, wasps	anti-histamines may be given immediately. In the case of a severe reaction desensitisation should be done.
Infectious hepatitis	gamma globuline (a concentrated human blood product)
Measles (if unimmunized)	gamma globulin
Meningococcal meningitis	sulfa is given by mouth to exposed children at the doctor's discretion
Rabies	vaccine and anti-serum. Immediate treatment.
Rheumatic fever	penicillin or sulpha drugs
Scarlet fever	penicillin or sulpha drugs
Snake bite	anti-venom injection
Streptococcal sore throat	penicillin or sulpha drugs
Tuberculosis	B.C.G. vaccine; this may be used when a child is likely to be exposed to tuberculosis.

Screening Tests

Tests designed to reveal an abnormality or illness not readily apparent to you, your child, or often the doctor himself, are called screening tests. Increasingly, they are being given by technicians rather than by nurses and doctors and for this reason it is hoped that they will be used more widely in the future. Some of the screening tests which your child might receive when he visits a doctor's office or a health clinic are discussed briefly.

Height and Weight — at each visit a child should be weighed in underwear and measured with shoes off. Since children vary in bone structure and body build there will be, of course, differences in the height and weight of children the same age.

At each health visit the doctor will observe a child for crossing of the eyes and check for normal *Vision and Hearing*. Special tests of vision and hearing including a test for color blindness can be given when a child is about school age.

Developmental Tests — the abilities of a child are checked or measured for language, in use of his hands and eyes, his balance and his coordination. These may be done yearly.

A *Tuberculin Test* — usually carried out at one year, and may be requested at intervals depending on the individual child and where he lives.

A *Urine Test* — usually done at age one, and once a year after that. This may reveal kidney disease or the presence of diabetes.

Blood Tests for Anemia — carried out yearly at the discretion of the doctor. Testing for sugar in the blood may also be carried out at his discretion.

Chest X-Rays — may be done at the doctor's discretion.

Dental Examinations — usually begin when a child is about two and one-half years old, and then every six months following, on the recommendation of the dentist.

Although physicians and public health personnel should keep records on each child's visit and his health status, you too should keep an accurate report of your child's growth and development, immunizations and illnesses; this information should be kept in a safe place, perhaps along with the birth certificate; it may be needed, for example, when your child has to be seen by another doctor who does not have immediate access to the health records. The child who has good health supervision by a public health clinic or physician will still become sick on occasion, but you, the doctor, and your child will be better prepared to cope with the illness. Health workers, knowing your child's specific health needs, will be able to care for him better, and you yourself will have learned how to help your child through the illness.

CHAPTER 3

Your Child's Food

By the time your child is one year of age he should be eating a number of foods. He has been having semi-solid foods for several months, and probably is taking milk from a cup. Gradually you are increasing the amount of solid foods you give him. On regular three meals a day, perhaps with planned between-meal lunches, he should be

having milk, fruits and vegetables, cereal and bread, meat, fish, eggs, and cheese, and 400 International Units of vitamin D. If this is so, he is on the road to good nutrition. He is eating that variety of foods outlined in Canada's Food Guide (see page 39) — a nutrition pattern based on the best scientific and nutritional advice available, and recommended for the whole family.

As you continue to follow this guide to good eating, you will provide your child with the proper nourishment for growth of his muscles, bones and teeth, for blood, and for his activity and general health.

The nutritional aspects of child care are most important and require attention in order:

1. to meet his immediate needs for normal physical development, to keep him well, and to get over colds and other sicknesses, and to give him energy for running, climbing and pushing.

2. to lay the foundation for good eating habits throughout life, to have a healthy attitude to food and mealtimes, and an interest in different kinds of foods.

This two-fold objective requires consideration, not only to food selection and menu planning, but to the growth and developmental patterns of children in these early months.

Developing Good Food Habits

Although each child is a unique person and will relate to food and eating in his own particular way and at his own speed, there are general patterns of behaviour which most children follow. As they begin to show their independence, they have their own idea of what, and how they want to eat. Awareness of what might be expected from a child as he advances from one to three years of age especially, can help parents adapt their feeding practices, leading to good nutrition and good food habits.

Decrease in Rate of Growth and in Appetite

Instead of eating with great enthusiasm your child of about one year of age or older may have a small appetite. This is because his rate of growth is slowing down and he actually needs less food in proportion to his body size than he did a few months before. He will vary in the amount he wishes to eat from day to day. He is also beginning to express preference for some foods. He may take a sudden dislike to his favorite foods, perhaps his cereal; he may go on eating "jags" wanting only one food, such as bananas or eggs. His behaviour may change from meal to meal. If he is teething, his appetite may be affected and he may miss a meal occasionally.

It helps to remember that ups and downs in appetite are normal. Often, it is during this early developmental stage that problems begin because parents do not realize that these are normal variations. If mother becomes worried and urges the child to eat larger servings, or tries to force rejected foods, the child may become more stubborn and trouble may begin. The more she frets and worries, the less he eats and consequently mother becomes anxious. Mealtime can become unpleasant and with it the danger of an unhappy relationship between mother and child about food and mealtimes. Such conflicts can lead to other behaviour problems.

Retained Interest in Bottle

Not all children are through with bottle feeding by one year. Some seem to need a certain amount of sucking and may continue to cling to some bottle feedings, especially the bedtime bottle. That is all right as long as other foods appropriate to his age are not neglected. However, he can be encouraged to drink from a cup; a small mug or glass that he can handle should be provided.

Lessened Interest in Food

As a child's appetite decreases, he becomes very busy at mealtimes — playing with food, dropping things, twisting, turning and standing up. If a child loses interest in eating, assume he has had enough; children usually eat the amount they seem to need. In a friendly manner let him out of his chair to walk around and play. Remove the meal without comment or impatient gestures. If he immediately starts clamouring for more food give him a second chance. But if he shows no more interest, do not try again. A consistent attitude of firmness within reason is the one most advisable.

A little one-year-old does a lot of experimenting with his hands. He may want to squeeze the food through his fingers, put a handful in his mouth, snatch the spoon and stick it into the food. If he succeeds in getting some to his mouth he will likely try again. The one-year-old is full of ambition. Provide bite-sized finger foods to encourage hand use at this stage.

Doing on His Own

It may be weeks before he can manage to twist his wrist, hold the spoon right side up and succeed in getting some to his mouth. Give him  a little time alone to feed himself and later, quietly take over. The more expert he gets, the longer she should have to feed himself. Do not expect steady progress and remember that when a child is tired or sleepy, he needs your help. Though he is trying very hard you can expect the child to be messy for a good while. Trying to force him to feed himself, scolding, hurrying, or constantly correcting him is not helping him to learn what should be a pleasant experience. Your child's desire to feed himself is just what you want, so let him do as much as he can.

Suitable utensils help the learning process along; for example, a low mug with a handle that is easy to hold and an unbreakable plate with straight sides are useful. When he can manage a serving of his favourite food in about ten minutes or less, he should be ready to handle the entire meal. Once he is on his own, allow him to pass up certain foods rather than stepping in to feed him the foods you want him to eat. Balance the meals as best you can from among the foods he most enjoys now. He will come around to accepting other foods in time. Parents who insist upon certain foods are likely to build up in the child a resistance to these, perhaps causing difficulty later on. On the other hand, parents should not make easily available those food items which give little more than calories and which a child might prefer, such as candies, potato chips, soft drinks, popsicles, very sweet desserts, etc. Because a child is governed by taste alone, he needs direction from parents. It is desirable that children associate this type of food with special events rather than with everyday eating.

Parents may make use of the following suggestions to assist children in this phase of their development.

Serene Atmosphere and Comfort at the Table — A quiet atmosphere is best for good mealtimes. This does not mean a solemn time, but a happy, enjoyable one. The period just before meals is an important one. Plan about half an hour of quiet activity for your child at that time. As a child grows from a small chair to a larger one, it may be necessary to place a hard cushion, a box or book to raise him to the table level so he can use his hands and elbows comfortably and with ease.

Happy and Regular Mealtimes — If a small child must wait too long for food when he is hungry, he may have little or no appetite when the food finally arrives. Also, irregular mealtimes frequently lead to haphazard eating between meals. Some conflict at mealtimes is bound to occur. If upsets persist to the discomfort of others, in spite of all the care you have taken to provide for your child's growing personality, they must be managed firmly. This becomes a necessity in order to keep mealtime a satisfying and pleasurable experience; also it will help the child to know his own value and the worth of others. When a child changes from his own table to the family table will vary from child to child and family to family. In any case, it will be gradual, perhaps by his joining the family towards the end of a meal, then a Sunday dinner or lunch, sharing in the sociability of the meal hour. He should be made to feel happy and secure, without fuss or over-attention, and should an accident occur, he should not be made fun of or scolded.

Choice of Foods —Children are sensitive to colour and texture. Usually they dislike foods that are too runny, too lumpy, or too stiff, and many children dislike mixtures. Food should be lukewarm, cut or chopped into manageable pieces, easy to chew and varied in texture. Foods containing bones should not be used, unless bones are carefully removed. Too large a serving of any food may discourage a child. Children enjoy familiar foods; they do not need as wide a variety as adults to maintain their interest.

Introducing New Foods — Although most children like to continue eating only familiar foods, they will enjoy new ones when these are given gradually in small amounts, along with a food they know. A child may just look at the new food and feel it the first time it is served; if it is served again he may more readily accept it, especially if other members of the family are enjoying their portions.

Learning to Chew — Although most children have been eating semi-solid foods for several months before the age of one, they should not be kept on mashed and strained food too long, otherwise they will not learn to chew. Parents must encourage the child to chew, by giving him time, and the kinds of food which require chewing, for example, a piece of toast, a cookie, or a wedge of apple, and let him bite off what he wants. If your child is a lazy chewer, he will need a lot of encouragement. It does not seem to work to wait for him to change by himself. You may start his meal with something he must chew.

Eating Between Meals — Many children, especially those one to three, need more than three meals a day in order to keep up their energy. Wholesome lunches or snacks may be given, such as milk, cheese, raw fruits or vegetables, fruits or juices, cereals with or without milk, simple cookies, crackers or toast. Lunches should be served at a regular time so as not to interfere with meals and in order to avoid nibbling. Gradually the number of between-meal lunches can be reduced and maybe eliminated.

Imitating a Good Example — A child watches his parents and other adults do and mimics them. Many a child has poor food habits due to the poor example of others. Parents should be sure that their own food habits are worth copying.

Meal Planning

Because the one-year-old is growing and developing and relating in new ways to food and everything pertaining to eating, you are giving him special consideration to ensure the formation of good habits. However, his food should not differ greatly from the food served to the rest of the family. Of course, learning to eat the foods of the rest of the family is a gradual process. The child, one and older, does not need different meals but will require less food than other members of the family. Some foods will be eliminated, for example, tea, coffee, rich foods; others can be cooked with less seasoning or served in a simpler form depending on the child's age and stage of development. Foods like nuts, popcorn, corn-kernels, that may cause children to choke should not be given to those under three years of age.

It is not always easy to prepare family meals and make modifications for each child's pattern of development and his personal tastes, but it is well worth striving for. Variety in selecting foods, such as those included in Canada's Food Guide, is the key, with quantity usually looked after by appetite and activity. Care is needed in preparing and cooking foods, especially fruits and vegetables, to retain their food value.

CANADA'S FOOD GUIDE

These Foods are Good to Eat.

Eat Them Every Day for Health.

Have Three Meals Each Day.

MILK

Children (up to about 11 years) ....2½ cups (20 fl. oz.)
Adolescents 4   cups (32 fl. oz.)
Adults ....1½ cups (12 fl. oz.)
Expectant and nursing mothers....4   cups (32 fl. oz.)

FRUIT

Two servings of fruit or juice including a satisfactory source of vitamin C (ascorbic acid) such as oranges, tomatoes, vitaminized apple juice.

VEGETABLES

One serving of potatoes.
Two servings of other vegetables, preferably yellow or green and often raw.

BREAD AND CEREALS

Bread (with butter or fortified margarine).
One serving of whole grain cereal.

MEAT AND FISH

One serving of meat, fish or poultry.
Eat liver occasionally.
Eggs, cheese, dried beans or peas, may be used in place of meat.
In addition, eggs and cheese each at least three times a week.

VITAMIN D — 400 International Units, for all growing persons and expectant and nursing mothers.

A Meal Pattern — The following pattern of meals for the family is based on Canada's Food Guide and indicates how you may distribute the essential foods throughout the day.

Breakfast	Lunch or Supper	Dinner
fruit or juice containing vitamin C	meat, egg, cheese or other protein food	meat, fish, cheese, or other protein food
whole grain or enriched cereal with milk	vegetable	potato
toast	bread	
	butter or margarine	other vegetable
butter or margarine		fruit or dessert
milk	dessert	milk
	milk	

Between-meal lunches of suitable foods (see page 37) may be served mid-morning, mid-afternoon, and evening if desired.

From this general meal pattern any number of suitable meals can be planned for the child from one to six years of age. Interesting choices can be made of different kinds of milk and milk products, fruits, vegetables, cereals, meat, poultry, fish. They can be prepared and served in a variety of ways, adapted to the child's age and stage, the family situation, and budget. Sizes of servings will differ — small, for very young children, larger or second servings for older ones.

Soups and sandwiches are popular with children as lunch or supper items, but care should be taken to make them nutritious, that is, soups containing a good supply of meat, vegetables or milk, are preferable to thin, "watery" soups, which give a feeling of fullness but little nourishment. Sandwich fillings ought to provide a generous serving of the selected protein food, for example, meat, egg, cheese.

One example of a day's menus is suggested and can be made to suit the age and appetite of any child.

Breakfast	Dinner	Supper
orange juice	beef patty	cream of tomato soup
oatmeal porridge with milk	baked potato	
	green beans	soft cooked egg
milk	carrots	bread - margarine
toast - margarine	milk pudding	canned peach
	milk	milk

Mid-morning	Mid-afternoon
apple juice	small glass of milk
	cookie

Nutrients — Functions — Sources

When you plan your meals using Canada's Food Guide as a basis, as suggested above, you are selecting foods which will provide the body with the nutrients considered essential for health. Briefly stated, these nutrients, their main functions and food sources are as follows:

Nutrients	Main Functions	Some Main Food Sources
Protein	build, repair, energy	milk, meats, fish, eggs, cheese, cereals, some vegetables
Fats	energy	margarine, butter, fats in meat, fish, whole milks and their products
Carbohydrates	energy	cereals, breads, fruits, vegetables, sweets
Iron	formation of hemoglobin in red blood cells	liver, other meats, eggs, whole grain and enriched cereals, infant cereals, green vegetables, dried fruit
Calcium	development of bones and teeth	milk, cheese
Phosphorus	development of bones and teeth	milk, egg yolk, fish, whole grain cereals
Vitamin A	• growth; health of mucous membrane • prevention of a type of night blindness	liver, fish liver oils, green and yellow vegetables, yellow fruits, eggs, whole milk, butter, fortified margarine
Thiamine	• utilization of food energy	pork, heart, legumes, whole grain and enriched cereals
Riboflavin	• health of eye and skin tissue	milk, cheese, liver, other meats
Niacin	• utilization of food energy	liver, other meats, fish, whole grain and enriched cereals
Vitamin C	• prevention of scurvy • tooth structure	citrus fruits (orange, lemon, grapefruit), vitaminized apple juice, tomato and tomato juice, raw turnip, potato
Vitamin D	• utilization of calcium and phosphorus • prevention of rickets	fish liver oils, some milks, some margarine, sardines, salmon

A Word of Caution

Nutritional Anemia — There are some children who suffer from nutritional anemia. Of course, if mother notices that a child has a poor appetite, is listless and fatigued she should report this to the doctor. If he is found to be anemic, the doctor may prescribe an iron containing medicine. This is in addition to a good varied diet based on Canada's Food Guide, containing such iron rich foods as meats, eggs, enriched and whole grain cereals and bread, dried fruits and vegetables.

Filling Up On Milk — Sometimes, if a child drinks a lot of milk, parents feel secure that he is being well nourished. This may well be so, but a child can drink so much that he has no appetite for the other necessary foods. In this situation, it is wise to withhold milk until other foods have been eaten. Milk is a highly nutritious food but it contains practically no iron. When skimmed or partially skimmed milks are used, the intake of vitamin A may be lessened due to the removal of fat. Unless these milks have had vitamin A added to them, as permitted by regulations, other sources must be eaten, for example, green and yellow vegetables, fortified margarine, butter, whole milk, cheese, eggs, liver.

Scurvy — Unfortunately, this deficiency disease is still being found among children of six months to two years of age. It has long been known that vitamin C (ascorbic acid) will prevent this condition. Every child needs this vitamin every day and he will be protected by eating a daily food source such as citrus fruit (orange, grapefruit) or their juices (two ounces) or vitaminized apple juice (four ounces). Since vitamin C is easily destroyed, care must be taken to keep the foods containing it cool and covered; they should not be heated or boiled.

If, under the physician's supervision your child has been receiving vitamin C in, for example, drops or enriched formula, make sure a good source is given to him as he begins to eat like the rest of the family.

Overweight and Underweight — A fat baby is not necessarily a healthy baby. Overweight infants tend to become overweight children and overweight adults. It is advisable to have children maintain a weight that will allow them to carry out their play activities with energy and zest. It is not a good idea to allow a child to eat large quantities of food — more than is needed, nor to eat foods high in fat and sugar content. He may become overweight, become used to large amounts of foods and foods which are sweet or appeal to him at the time, and may have difficulty cutting down later.

Vitamin D — 400 International Units daily are needed all the time your child is growing, for the formation and growth of bones and teeth and to prevent rickets, a disease still occurring among Canadian children. Usually vitamin D is taken in liquid, drop or capsule form. Ask your doctor about the sources he would recommend. It is wasteful and can be dangerous to give your child an excess of vitamin D.

Regulations permit the addition of this vitamin to margarine and to all forms of milk. Although by no means general at present, milk enriched with vitamin D is being sold in a number of communities. To know whether the milk you are buying contains vitamin D, you must read the labels on the milk containers. If your child is receiving each day two and one half cups (the quantity of milk recommended in Canada's Food Guide) of vitamin D enriched milk, he will not need a supplement. If this is not the case, a supplement providing 400 International Units daily should be given to him.

Further Help

The importance of a child's nutrition cannot be stressed enough, for good health is impossible without good nutrition. All parents want their children to be well nourished and free of feeding problems. These goals can be reached by following the guidance of your physician and by making use of sound nutrition information. For further details on nutrition, it is suggested that you get in touch with your provincial or local health department.

CHAPTER 4

Your Child's Teeth

The years from one to six are very important for the development of good permanent teeth. These years are vital for the protection of your child's foundation, primary, or "baby" teeth which were formed before his birth and are all completed and in place in his mouth before he reaches three. His permanent or secondary teeth begin to harden by absorbing calcium shortly after his birth. The enamel or the outer covering of the crown of the tooth is completely formed by the end of the eighth year, except on the wisdom teeth or third molars. The roots are completed after the teeth appear in the mouth.

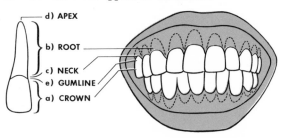

d) APEX
b) ROOT
c) NECK
e) GUMLINE
a) CROWN

During development, the teeth are very sensitive to the supply of calcium and phosphorus as well as vitamins A, C, D, and fluorine. Once the teeth are completed calcium cannot be added to the enamel by increasing the amount of calcium in the diet. Unlike bones, teeth cannot replace their calcium which is lost through decay. Even the completed parts of the enamel of the secondary teeth before they break through the gums cannot be affected by diet.

Diet

The food guide recommended in Chapter 3 should be closely followed. Calcium, phosphorus, and vitamins A, C, D, and fluorine are the nutritional factors which are most important in tooth development and the health of the gums. Coarse, fibrous foods such as firm raw fruits and vegetables, besides having a good cleansing action on the teeth, also play an important part in the development of the jaws to provide ample room and support for the teeth. Sticky sweet foods have a bad effect on the teeth; they are the main cause of tooth decay. Too many sweet foods and drinks may also make your child neglect important foods. A child may enjoy sweets, but moderation is desirable. Repeated eating of sweets during the day is more harmful than having one sweet at the end of a meal. The best dessert is a cleansing food such as fresh fruit.

Primary Teeth

It is essential that your child retain his foundation teeth and keep them clean and in good repair until they are ready to be shed in the natural way. The following are good reasons for their preservation:

1. Teeth are needed for chewing food thoroughly and comfortably.

Chewing food to prepare it for digestion is important. Your child has to replace his body tissue which he wears out during his daily activities and he also has to provide material for his daily growth. A child may not chew his food well, because he is unable to chew comfortably on decayed, painful teeth.

The loss or serious decay of one of the eight primary molars decreases by almost one-third the grinding power of your child's first set of teeth. This decrease occurs because each foundation tooth has two grinding partners in the opposite jaw. When one tooth is lost, its two partners in the opposite jaw have only an empty space to grind on.

The expression "it is just a baby tooth" is often used as an excuse to overlook decay in these first teeth. Remember, however, "baby" teeth are an important foundation for a set of strong and regular secondary teeth later on.

2. Good primary teeth help develop strong and regular secondary teeth.

It is important to keep the primary teeth in good condition until they are ready to be shed naturally. The early loss of a tooth is usually followed by the drifting of its neighbour, which closes the space where the tooth was prematurely lost. If one of your child's primary teeth has been lost, it may be necessary for the dentist to maintain the space by a space maintainer to allow room for the permanent tooth that will take its place later.

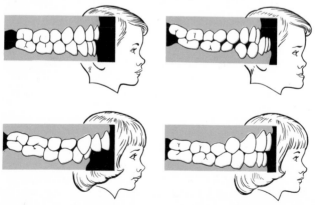

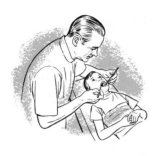

When the succeeding tooth to a primary tooth grows in, if there is not enough room it may be crowded out towards the cheek or in towards the tongue and the other permanent teeth forced out of their correct position. Such crowding can cause jaw problems and deformities. Many cases of crowded teeth requiring braces have their origin in the early loss of foundation teeth. There are also factors which interfere with the proper cutting of your child's secondary teeth and a dentist can recognize these problems early if you visit him on a regular basis.

3. Good Dental Health Adds to Attractiveness

Normal speech development depends on complete dental arches to permit the tongue to form certain sounds. Early loss of primary teeth very frequently leads to bad speech habits which often persist.

Good appearance results when sound primary and secondary teeth are in proper position.

Certain childhood habits such as thumb sucking, lip, cheek and tongue biting, mouth breathing and tongue thrusting, if continued too long or in excess, may cause tooth and facial deformities. The correction of such habits calls for the advice of both the physician and the dentist. Usually, methods are suggested which will attract the least attention to the habit and reduce as far as possible the child's feelings of frustration and unhappiness.

4. Good foundation teeth avoid toothaches.

Anyone who has experienced the severe pain of a toothache should consider this one reason alone as sufficient to warrant caring for foundation teeth to avoid their decay. Pain, loss of sleep and emotional strain can interfere with your child's good health.

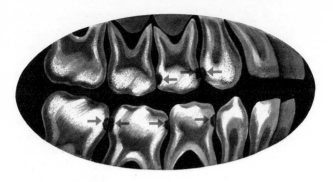

Decay of Teeth

Tooth decay attacks more people than any other disease except the common cold. Colds come and go, giving us periods of freedom in between; tooth decay, once it begins, never heals. About 99 people out of every 100 in Canada have tooth decay at some time in their lives. It begins very early in childhood. Many children by the age of three already have a cavity or cavities. Every child between the ages of two and three should start a program of regular dental care.

A cavity is never too small to fill. Do not wait until they are so large that you can see them; it may be too late then. Very small cavities cannot be seen. The dentist requires a fine pointed instrument or x-rays to find them, especially when they are between the teeth. Cavities can

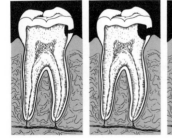
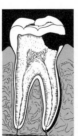
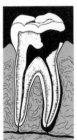

be filled at this stage more quickly, and with more comfort for your child and at less expense to yourself. Neglected cavities become larger and deeper, finally reaching the nerve or pulp, which is then attacked by bacteria. The infection continues on down through the nerve canal and out into the jaw bone around the end of the root, causing an abscess. Regular six-month dental examinations enable the dentist to find any cavities before they become large enough to cause a toothache or abscess.

Your Child and the Dentist

Modern preventive dentistry can be a comfortable and interesting experience for your child. He must not develop fears from a discussion of pain, or lose his confidence in

you or the dentist by being deceived or told untruths. Be strictly honest with him. If the dentist finds it necessary to cause discomfort or pain he will inform your child in advance. However, if visits are regular, two or three times a year, the treatment will be minor and rarely uncomfortable.

After the first visit, you should remain in the waiting room, unless the dentist requires your presence in the inner office.

Permanent Molars

Between five and seven years of age, the first secondary or permanent molars appear back of the primary molar teeth. They do not take the place of any foundation teeth but come in directly. They are the first secondary teeth to appear. These first permanent molars are among the most important teeth in your child's mouth as they influence normal jaw development. They are very susceptible to decay. The dentist should see these molars every six months.

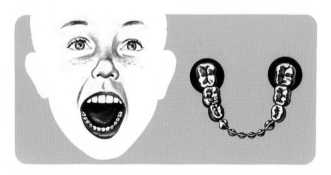

Mouth Hygiene

The habit of brushing the teeth should be shown to a child as soon as his teeth appear. Have the dentist

teach him the proper use of the toothbrush and repeat this yourself following the instructions below (see also Chapter 2). The teeth should be brushed immediately after eating. Brush the teeth the way they grow, down from the gums for upper teeth and up from the gums for lower teeth.

Thorough tooth brushing is very important in the prevention of tooth decay. A further reason for brushing

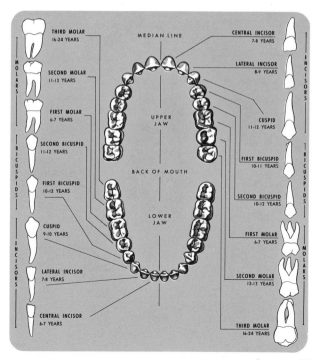

THIRD MOLAR
16-24 YEARS

SECOND MOLAR
11-13 YEARS

FIRST MOLAR
6-7 YEARS

SECOND BICUSPID
11-12 YEARS

FIRST BICUSPID
10-12 YEARS

CUSPID
9-10 YEARS

LATERAL INCISOR
7-8 YEARS

CENTRAL INCISOR
6-7 YEARS

MEDIAN LINE

UPPER JAW

BACK OF MOUTH

LOWER JAW

CENTRAL INCISOR
7-8 YEARS

LATERAL INCISOR
8-9 YEARS

CUSPID
11-12 YEARS

FIRST BICUSPID
10-11 YEARS

SECOND BICUSPID
10-12 YEARS

FIRST MOLAR
6-7 YEARS

SECOND MOLAR
12-13 YEARS

THIRD MOLAR
16-24 YEARS

MOLARS   BICUSPIDS   INCISORS

INCISORS   BICUSPIDS   MOLARS

is to massage the gums, and give the gums a healthy firmness.

A good dentifrice can be made at home using one teaspoon of baking soda to two teaspoons of table salt. There are many toothpastes available, flavoured and scented to make them pleasant tasting. Careful brushing of the teeth immediately after eating is stressed; if not possible, the mouth should be rinsed with water.

The Use of Fluoride

A water supply which contains sufficient fluoride helps prevent dental cavities. Resistance to cavities acquired by a child who drinks fluoridated water when his teeth are developing carries over into adult life. A child who starts drinking fluoridated water after his teeth are formed can still receive some benefit. If your water supply does not contain fluoride, the dentist or dental hygienist may apply a fluoride solution to your child's teeth at regular intervals. The use of a toothpaste containing fluoride is another method of helping to protect teeth against decay.

CHAPTER 5

Your Child's Safety

Accidents cause more deaths among Canadian children over the age of one year than any single disease, and many more children are injured.

Many accidents which occur inside the home are due to neglect and can be prevented. Anticipation of the way your naturally curious child behaves will help prevent

most avoidable accidents. As your child grows and develops, he must learn to recognize dangers about him and he must learn to play and work in such a way as to avoid them. Your protection, example, and teaching will help him develop safe living habits.

By one, your child is ready to begin his training for safety, but he needs continuing protection by adults. During his second year he is walking although unsteadily at first. He is interested in everything about him, and his curiosity leads him to feel, taste, and move everything he can reach. He is a great climber; on and off chairs, in and out of bed, up and down stairs. He plays outdoors now and is fascinated by the busy street. The toddler learns by doing: this is the only way he can learn. You must allow your child to move, touch and try, but you must also watch him.

The older three to six-year-old child learns accident prevention from observation, and from protection with supervised freedom. He is very active, curious and unpredictable; he runs rather than walks, and acts before he thinks. He spends much of his time playing with other children at home, at his friends', in parks or playgrounds. He loves tricycles, wagons or scooters. He climbs and explores. He loves to imitate his parents. Little boys will try to do what their fathers do, whether it is washing the car or do-it-yourself carpentry, while little girls will play house. Children can be taught to do all the things they want to do in a way that is safe and satisfying. Example is a fine teacher.

Your child will explore and learn with all his faculties including his eyes, tongue and hands. He has a keen interest and no sense of danger. Instead of forbidding an act, show him how to accomplish it safely. As he learns, change instructions to reminders. Of course some accidents are necessary for the natural process of growing up. While we want our children to live, we also want them to learn from experience. We do not want to overprotect them to the point where they are unaware of dangers.

Your young child should not be left alone in the house at any time. If you must leave a child at home, have a responsible person you can trust (not another child) left in charge. You must be continually on guard; allow your child experiences, but under supervision. Accidents can be avoided! Look at your home surroundings from time to time to see how safe it is for your child to live in. When visiting in other surroundings also watch for new hazards.

Traffic Safety

Your preschooler must be taught the basic rules of street safety by your own example. Do not let him cross the street alone. Take his hand and show and explain to him why he must always stop and look both ways before crossing.

Many children are killed or injured every year by automobiles. Some of these accidents are the fault of the driver, but most of them are caused by children's carelessness — a child running out into the street from behind a parked car to retrieve his ball. Do not let your child play in these areas without supervision. Teach him to watch for cars in the driveway.

In an automobile, never let a child stand or put his head or arms out of the windows while the car is moving. If a child misbehaves while the car is in motion, pull over to the side and stop until you have the problem settled. He should be restrained by a good safety harness or safety seat. Adults should set a good example by wearing seat belts. They should also be in a position to hold on to a child should this become necessary. Never leave a child alone unsupervised in a car. Be sure to take the key out of the ignition when you get out of the car. Leave the car in gear on level ground, not on a hill, with parking brakes on.

Safety in the Out-of-Doors

Your child will want to play outdoors daily. This is very natural and good for him, but be sure he plays where he can be kept away from the street by a sturdy fence with no easy foot-holds. The yard should be clear of glass and jagged edged cans. Children should not play where there are deep ditches, ponds, uncovered wells, old refrigerators, or old stoves.

Accidents are more frequent when a child's playmates are older. A two or three year old may be easily hurt by baseball bats, hard balls, big bicycles and rough play.

As your child grows older, he should be taught to climb and to get down again; to test foot holds on trees or fences and to come down in an area free from jagged rocks or sharp objects. Teach him to recognize safe and unsafe things to climb, for example, by pointing out dead limbs in a tree. He should learn to expect falls so that he will be less frightened, more relaxed and therefore, less likely to receive serious injury.

If your child is learning to ride his tricycle or wagon, teach him on the sidewalk if there is no other place available. Explain to him that it is dangerous to ride on the street and driveway, and be sure he observes safety precautions.

Teach your child to swim and to respect water safety rules. Remember water can be dangerous, even in a bathtub. Always test bath water before allowing your child to get in and do not leave him in the bathtub unsupervised.

Fire, Burns and Cuts

Matches and cigarette lighters must be kept away from children, because they are fascinated by flame but do not know its danger. Teach your child to blow out matches and candles in your presence. Remove fire hazards by placing screens before open fires, and guards in front of hot water radiators and electric wall heaters with open elements.

Preschoolers like to help around the house. Use this desire to teach the safe handling of simple household equipment and tools. A preschooler is not ready however, to handle electrical equipment of any kind. Knives, scissors or other sharp tools should be kept in a safe place out of reach. Protect your child from investigating on his own the washing machine, dryer or electric iron by showing it to him before he gets too curious.

In the kitchen, place the pots containing hot liquids back from the stove or table edge with handles turned in. Prevent the danger of fire by fixing faulty stoves, electric sockets and cords. Keep out of reach electric cords attached to appliances that could fall on a child if he pulls the cord. Cover electric outlets with adhesive tape until your child is old enough to understand their use.

Carelessly placed paper and magazines can start a fire in a minute. Empty your ash trays into a metal container. A fire extinguisher, regularly checked to make sure it will always be in good working condition, is a wonderful protection against serious fires.

Falls

Young children are bound to have many tumbles and falls since they like to push and pull, roll and climb, kick and jump. Nature protects your child during these "experimental" years because his body structure is somewhat flexible. His bones are soft so they do not break easily and his joints and muscles are loose. Consequently, fractures and dislocations are not common in young children unless there is a really severe blow or fall; but bumps and bruises do occur frequently.

To protect your young child from falls, secure doors that lead to stairways, driveways, and storage areas. Use fasteners that are out of a small child's reach. Make sure your rugs are tacked down or skid-proof. Put gates on porches and stairways and keep window and door screens locked or nailed securely. It is wise to arrange your furniture so that your child is not tempted to climb from one piece to another.

Do not let a preschooler carry bottles, sharp instruments or hot foods or liquids which may harm him if he falls. It is best not to let him walk around with a spoon, bottle or stick in his mouth in case he falls. Teach him to put away his toys for his and your safety. Once your child learns to practise safety in his daily activities he will take pride in his accomplishments.

Poisons

Your child likes to explore and will not be familiar with poisonous materials. All pills and medicines, regardless of the type, should be stored in a locked cupboard until your child is old enough to understand that there are many kinds of medicine and that some are dangerous. Throw all old medicines out and try to have child-proof containers provided for those medicines you do buy. A medicine cabinet with a lock is an extra safeguard, but only if it is kept locked. Cleaning solutions, drain cleansers, lye, insecticides, disinfectants, lemon oil, kerosene, and other household poisons should also be stored well out of reach. Some cosmetics are also poisonous. It is wise to store the garden insecticides and fertilizers in a safe place.

Teach your child never to taste unidentified things he finds. Use lead-free paint to refinish furniture or toys, or to do any indoor painting.

If your child does swallow some poisonous material try to determine what substance was swallowed and keep the original container for the doctor. Immediately call your doctor, the local poison control centre, or the nearest hospital for advice.

It would be most helpful if young children could be spared the bad example all too often given them, of adults taking pills and other drugs. When medicines are pre-scribed for adults, they might better be taken in private.

Foreign Objects in the Mouth, Nose and Ears

Never give a plastic bag to a child or use it to cover a mattress or pillow because they cling to the nostrils and can cause smothering. Destroy plastic bags, tie them in a knot and throw them away. In cold weather leave a win-dow open a bit to ensure ventilation against any dangerous fumes which have no odour and give no warning. Blow up balloons before giving them to your child. If he tries to blow it up himself it may get caught in his throat and choke him. Peanuts and other foods on which a small child may choke have been mentioned on page 38. Keep small articles such as needles, coins and buttons in a safe place so your child does not swallow or choke on them, or put them in his nose or ears. With experience and guidance, your child will learn to become responsible for his own safety.

Keep all firearms and ammunition under lock and key. Children do not know the difference between play guns and real ones. There is a great need in today's world to teach children and adults alike to love and protect one another.

Be Prepared

Every family should have a set of important phone numbers placed in a safe, easily accessible spot.

List these telephone numbers:

The Doctor

The Hospital

Poison Control Centre (if one available)

Fire Department

Police Department

Ambulance Company

Taxi Company

Keep a first aid kit and a first aid booklet handy for emergency use.

A good first aid kit can be made containing the following:

Absorbent cotton

Soap, to be used with water for cleansing wounds

Sterile gauze pads

Bandages, 1" and 2"

Adhesive, 1"

Antiseptic solution

Tube of antibiotic ointment (recommended by your doctor)

Scissors

Bandaids for minor cuts

Emetic (ask your doctor about this)

Know when, why and how to use artificial respiration.

PART II

Behaviour

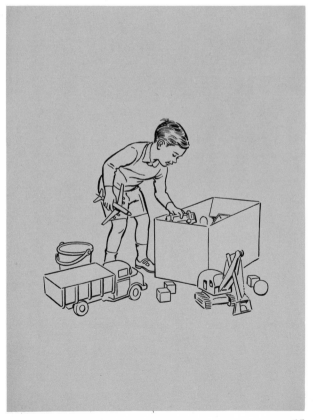

General Comments

Halfway up (apologies to A. A. Milne) the stairs
Is a stair
Where I sit.
There isn't any
Other stair
Quite like
It.

(A. A. Milne, "Halfway Down")

Rearing children can be one of the most enjoyable things parents ever do — helping a small, completely dependent baby grow and develop into an independent, mature adult. The job of being a parent does not need to be undertaken either in a spirit of grim determination or uneasy timidity. It is not a matter of following hard and fast rules. Experts today reassure parents that a common sense approach to child care is best. The parents who enjoy being parents will likely be good parents.

To rear a family successfully, however, parents do need to know what children are like, how they act and react, how they grow and develop and what behaviour is characteristic of different ages. Part II on Behaviour is written in terms of age to help you, as parents, relate the particular topics to your child. However, it is understood that behaviour is not sharply distinguishable at different ages. It is a continual process of growth related to experiences accumulated through life, with many differences existing among individual children. We are all interested in the good health and happiness of the whole child. Each topic has been treated separately, but keep in mind as you read that these are part of the larger whole — your child.

The child who is played with and hugged, who is physically well cared for and encouraged to learn for himself under his parents' open approval, will flourish physically and emotionally. You will enjoy watching your child when you observe that he learns by imitating and trying over and over again; that he learns with his whole body, with his mouth, his eyes and ears, his feet and hands. He learns from his contact with you and your attitude to him. You and your child can share in the triumphs of his own achievements when you share a feeling of effection, encouragement and understanding.

When you understand how your child develops best, you will find plenty of time to give him out of your busy day. The compromises you make now with such things as good housekeeping will pay dividends as your child grows up. You can manage to do a fair job of housekeeping and a good job of raising children, if you are sensible in accepting moderate standards of tidiness and cleanliness. Plan your work around your child's schedule rather than insisting on doing things at the usual, conventional time.

. . . All sorts of funny thoughts

Run round my head:

"It isn't really

Anywhere!

It's somewhere

Else instead!"

(A. A. Milne, "Halfway Down")

CHAPTER 6

Your One-Year-Old

At one year your baby becomes a toddler, a creeper and a climber. Daily life changes for him and the family. He is not content to stay in a controlled area, he wants to be free to explore everything he sees.

Once a child starts to become independent, he wants to run everything by himself, without mother. Parents are faced with the problem of how much to restrict and how much to give in to their child. A one-year-old needs lots of love and attention, but he also needs time to explore and play by himself. If parents understand their child's growth and behaviour, they will be better able to assist his emotional, physical and mental development.

A fussy, worrisome mother or relative who just cannot leave the young child alone, who is always interrupting his contented play to pick him up, bounce him around or hand him new toys, prevents the child from learning to amuse himself. A mother who is so wrapped up in her child that she follows him constantly on his explorings, for fear he will hurt himself, always offering help before it is called for, is not helping him to learn. This child may lose faith in himself and become submissive, always seeking approval before he tries anything new. Or he may feel he must battle for everything and become rebellious.

On the other hand, some mothers are too permissive. They give their child too many choices. They allow their child to express his emotions fully, even if it means listening to him howl his head off, believing it is best to let a child openly express his feelings. A child, however, must learn to respect and practise the social rules of society. It is better therefore, to learn how to divert his attention if his emotions get out of control. When he reaches school age, his teacher will not have the time or patience to let each child actively express his emotions. Love and understanding will help him become an active, outgoing and creative child.

Most of the rough spots in the toddler's day occur over routines — eating, dressing and sleeping. More and more your toddler is being drawn into the family routine. His activities no longer revolve around his own immediate needs; he has to fit into the family schedule. Your child no longer enjoys his position as a baby. At these times, you come closest to your toddler's efforts to balance his wish for independence with his need for continued close contact with his mother. He will be easier to manage during the difficult periods of the day if you arouse his interest in the next part of the routine.

The Adventure of Exploring

Everything is excitingly new to your one-year-old creeper. Absolutely everything within reach, and hopefully some out of reach, have to be examined. Your child just has to feel the size, shape and texture of everything. Once a child is out of a controlled play area mothers exclaim "he's into everything" . . . "he'll wreck the house" . . . "he'll hurt himself." Parents understand this is a child's natural way of learning about the world. He must feel and explore to learn the difference between objects and also right from wrong.

As soon as your creeper is given the freedom to explore, adjustments must be made. Valuables and dangerous objects such as ornaments and breakable ashtrays should be moved out of reach. Handles of pots and pans on the stove must be turned in. Since he is not old enough to know what is safe or unsafe, his area of exploration should be checked often for safety. (See Chapter 5 on Safety). The fewer things you have to teach him to leave alone the better. Your child's welfare, development, and safety, are worth some planning, some rearrangement of your possessions.

You, by handling the situation carefully in the beginning, can simplify the business of teaching your child to leave certain things alone. Let him do his early exploring wherever you happen to be working so that, from the background, you can readily keep an eye on his activities. Your toddler needs to be encouraged to satisfy his curiosity and interests in his own way — until his way interferes with the comfort of others, his own safety or the family routine of living. Your child can sometimes be distracted from one kind of activity by your suggesting something else. However, when he has tackled something that is too much for him to handle, give him a helping hand in his investigation. Your words of caution about such things as floor lamps and washing machines make him understand that certain objects are not playthings. Once his first curiosity is satisfied and you have explained and cautioned him, he will not be as likely to get into trouble the minute your back is turned.

Being a young explorer takes lots of independence and courage. Sometimes the vastness of his world and his own helplessness are overwhelming and he howls for mother — his base of operations, his main source of security. Your toddler will alternately give you the brush-off and then cry soon after you are out of sight. Letting him cry it out does not always help, it hinders his growing independence. Independence grows as he is encouraged to find things for himself, to explore with the comfortable feeling of knowing that you are right at hand if needed. He is beginning to realize how much he loves and needs you. This clinging phase may be inconvenient but it will not last forever.

Walking

Walking is one of life's most exciting achievements. Parents and their young children both take pride in the first steps.

Most children learn to walk somewhere between 12 and 15 months, a few as early as nine months, and quite a number of bright, healthy children will not walk until 18 months or even later. There are many reasons for wide variations in the starting age. One active muscular child may walk early while another equally developed child may be getting around on all fours so well that he postpones trying. Illness or a bad fall experienced during the first trials may cause your child to put off walking for a while. A heavy child will likely start walking late.

As soon as your child learns to walk, he will want to go everywhere. There are so many interesting things around. He needs the muscle-strengthening exercise or running around. Your toddler should have the chance to run freely so that he can gain strength and skill. It is normal for a child, when he starts walking, to plant his legs far apart, to bend his knees a little, to support his weight on the full soles of his feet and to toe-out. His feet, however, will soon straighten around to a parallel position. If you notice that your child has sagging ankles, knock-knees or that he toes-out, consult your doctor about this at the next visit.

Less Controlled Play

Once your child has started to walk he may become unhappy playing in a small restricted area. You should not leave your child in such a space for too long, especially when his need for freedom is increasing. Children vary; some, at a year and a half are still content in one area; others at less than a year are trying to go everywhere. Usually, they gradually grow tired of a limited play space and their period of happy play grows shorter each day. As with all other phases of growing up, an alert mother takes her lead from her child. When your child shows definite signs of impatience in his particular play area, try a change of toys. If that does not work, then he has had enough for the time being and needs to have more freedom.

Out of the Carriage

As often as you can spare the time on shopping trips and walks, your toddler may be allowed some time out of  the carriage. For him it is both exercise and adventure. Mothers in a hurry to get the shopping done complain about the time this takes. To you it seems like a waste of time, but to your young explorer it is a succession of fascinating discoveries. He will want to wander along and conduct a lengthy inspection of such things as a twig or caterpillar. He just will not be hurried. Scolding or nagging is not the answer. You should decide how long you can give your child out of the carriage on such trips. Then while he is out, interfere as little as possible and keep his exploring free and happy. You can easily bring him back to the carriage by telling him about the things to be seen on the rest of the trip.

Climbing

Climbing is fascinating to your toddler. It is wise to let him practise on low, safe chairs or stools. As soon as he is interested, let him practise going up and down stairs. Climbing helps develop a sense of balance. Of course, children at first tend to crawl upstairs and come down backwards.

Getting Dirty and Clean Again

Youngsters are eager learners and explorers, not dolls to be all dressed up for display. One-year-olds want and need to be allowed to do things where they can get

dirty. The slow and unsteady toddler will not mind one bit being rather grimy from frequent tumbles. He will just love to wade in puddles, squeeze mud through his fingers and toes, dig in the sand, and roll on the ground. If a child is constantly warned and prevented from becoming dirty, his personality may suffer. He may grow timid and fearful of trying anything new because he may get dirty. The wise mother will dress her child in practical, washable garments so that he may freely enjoy this normal part of growing up.

Getting dirty gives children an opportunity to learn to wash themselves. A young child naturally loves to play in water. Before two, he will start washing his own face and hands if soap and water are put at his level. A low bench with a basin of his own or a sturdy stool will help to bring him up to the big wash basin.

Sometime during bathing, your child will discover his sex organs. Girls and boys will want to explore their genitals just as thoroughly and with the same curiosity as they do the rest of their bodies. It is perfectly natural; it is perfectly normal. There is no need to interfere hastily. (See Chapter 8).

Young children become independent by doing simple everyday things for themselves, but they need time to learn. Soap and water is fascinating to the beginner. If your child can go at the business of washing himself leisurely, he will feel happy about his growing feeling of independence. After a reasonable time, your youngster can be gently steered on to something else by getting him talking about what to do next. To scold or hurry can spoil the nice spirit of cooperation.

Language Development

Young children enjoy making sounds such as cooing, shouting and babbling to amuse themselves. Before too long, children hit upon a great many sounds, some of which they will discard because they will not need them in learning their parents' language.

From an early age, stimulate your child's language and reasoning by talking to him and encouraging him in his attempts to talk. Children vary greatly in the age at which they start talking. Girls tend to talk earlier than boys and to be slightly better in language ability throughout these early years. The starting age for talking ranges widely. It may be as early as the eighth or not until the sixteenth month. Around one year, through the attention a child receives when he just happens to make a sound like a word, and through having it repeated back to him, he begins to associate words with objects and people. A child's first words generally refer to specific things such as "Mama" and "Dada". Some children first speak with a flow of non-words followed by a word. Your child will find that words are powerful and he may overdo it when he discovers the strength of "no." Often a child will let one word do the work of a whole sentence such as "go-go."

Your child will imitate the words you frequently use. Be sure you speak clearly, slowly and use words you want him to say. It will help if you speak to him in single words such as "go" ... "hot" ... "shoe". He may become frustrated if he cannot understand what you are saying or if he cannot make you understand what he is saying. Be patient and encourage him. Speaking is one of the ways your child shows what he is learning.

Which Hand?

Some children from the beginning have a strong preference for one hand. Other children continue to use either hand until they are about three and a few until they are older. A child's preferred hand may change several times in these early years. Some children feed themselves with the same hand used for feeding them.

Allow your child to use either hand, whichever is natural for him. A preference for the left hand will not prevent him from doing good school work or harm his athletic ability. Forcing a child to go against his natural tendency can be extremely upsetting to him. If he seems unable to settle on either hand you may wish to consult the doctor. Once your child has settled on one hand encourage him by handing him things to that hand.

Sleeping Habits

The one-year-old's changing schedule of sleep can be a bit hectic for you. Your child may rebel against his morning nap for a couple of weeks, then go back to it for a while. He is at the stage where two daytime naps are often too much and one not quite enough. However, most children will soon settle down to one rest a day. A lot of future problems can be avoided if you are friendly and flexible during the changing schedule. For a while, continue to try him out in the morning with a few toys in

the crib. He may play contentedly, and then drop off to sleep. If not, let him out when he grows restless. When he misses the morning sleep, it is a good idea to move the lunch hour forward and put him off to bed earlier in the afternoon.

Even though your child may not always sleep, a regular afternoon rest is a good thing. There is no need for concern when naps are occasionally missed. Your child will accept the afternoon in bed with toys and books as a comfortable routine. He will play contentedly by himself because he is not worried; no one has made him feel guilty about not sleeping. If his body needs sleep he will drop off. If not, perhaps he will rest for close to an hour before becoming restless and anxious to be up. After the afternoon rest, leave time for a little outdoor play before the evening meal.

Your child spends more hours lying flat in bed than in any other single position, hence correct sleeping posture is very important. A roomy crib with a firm spring and firm mattress is essential. There is no need to give your child a pillow. Heavy bed covers are uncomfortable and should be avoided since they restrict freedom of movement during sleep. His night garments should be loose. He should sleep alone in a bed large enough to allow for normal movement. Be sure the room he sleeps in is quiet so that he can sleep. However, normal household activity should be carried on; the child should not need absolute quiet during his rest or sleeping time.

When all is well in his world, your young child, groggy with sleep, just naturally welcomes being tucked in his own little bed at night. He does, that is, if his hours for sleeping have been regular and if going to bed has been made a pleasant experience.

On some special holiday or event, it is a good thing to let your children stay up to enjoy the excitement. However, it is not a good idea to have too many such occasions because children tend to waken at about the regular time the next morning and do not make up the lost sleep.

If you want your child to go to bed willingly, you must be careful not to let him think you are trying to get rid of him. A child who feels his parents are in a hurry to get him out of the way may be upset. Though heavy with fatigue, he will try to stay up as long as he can, and that may be for several hours! To swoop down upon a youngster saying, "Now away you go to bed", is to invite resistance. No matter how rushed you may be, the time spent now in keeping the bedtime parade peaceful and leisurely will pay off for years to come. Arguments started now about going to bed can go on and on. Your attitude is just as important as your words and actions.

With your one-year-old, show your interest in the toy with which he happens to be playing and if it is a small one, carry off your child and toy together. If he is playing with something too big, divert him to a smaller one before you gather him in your arms. With the older ones, sound an advance warning so they can be prepared to leave their play. To a child, play is not trivial; it is all-important. When it is time for him to stop, take a minute to enter into the spirit of his play, admire any construction, and still talking about his interest, lead him off to bed. Take it easy and he will be in a cooperative mood. Rush him or nag at him and he may resist bed.

Stories which are not too exciting, nursery rhymes, singing or just talking can help make bedtime a happy time. Children need to have the feeling of being close to their parents, of always having the reassurances of love and affection. Bedtime is a good time to give them this reassurance. It is relaxing.

Do not expect a child to go to sleep as soon as his head is down. Few children go to sleep quickly; usually they take about half an hour.

Your young child may start feeling a bit lonesome when he is put off to bed by himself. He may find it comforting to take things with him. It may be a stuffed doll, one particular blanket, several little trucks or even bigger toys. It is all right to let him, but observe common sense safety precautions. Things should be cleared away after he has dropped off to sleep.

When your child resists sleep, when he will not stay in bed and wakes up frequently in the night with no physical illness present, there is something wrong in his world. Be sure that his afternoon nap is not coming too late. Romping with father just before bedtime may be fun, but too stimulating. Instead, father can read, tell stories, or play music to give him just as much fun and be just as companionable. An unwise choice of radio or television programs could overexcite or depress him.

Your child may be tense or nervous because of his unhappy feelings. He may be afraid of the dark, afraid of being left alone or just plain lonely. He may be feeling angry if going to bed has developed into a fight. Somewhere there may be an unhappy family relationship, jealousy or a feeling of competition with a brother or sister, fear of a stern parent or a feeling of being not wanted, not loved.

Some children get up on their hands and knees to rock in bed, or roll their heads from side to side or bang their heads against the crib, at bedtime, during the day or after a nap. Some children do it only now and then, others, every day. Usually a child begins after the eighteenth month if he is going to do it at all and most children stop by two and one-half or three years. No one is really sure why children do this. It may first occur when your child is passing from one stage of development to another, such as from standing to walking, or if he is troubled or nervous. Boys tend to rock more than girls. If your child does rock or bang in bed, discuss it with your doctor.

The best cure, or preventive, for sleeping problems is to see that your child is getting plenty of affection, and that his feelings about you are not disturbed by battles over eating or toilet training. During the day, your child should have plenty of interesting play and be around other children. Being too strict does not help. If fear of the dark is a problem, try plenty of reassurance and leave the door open a bit. The light and sounds sifting in will be very reassuring. Usually a night light is unnecessary and best avoided.

Sleep can come easily and naturally to the healthy child who has had a busy day, who is sure of his parents' love and for whom bedtime has been made a pleasant experience.

Feeding

A child's nutrition with the formation of good food habits at an early age is a most important aspect of his growth and development. Considerable information on this subject, applicable to the child from one to six, is given in Chapter 3.

Toilet Habits

The time to start toilet training depends on the child. Until one year, a child's nervous system and muscle control are not developed enough to be able to stop a natural release. Before a year and a half, a child has no way of connecting "going to the toilet" with the feeling of having to go. So-called training earlier than this is really a chance matter of catching the movements of a child, who has them at regular times. Real bowel control can be taught to most children only after they have learned to walk.

The mother who wants her child to be happy will avoid at all costs letting her toilet training become a struggle between them. A child whose mother begins training too early or eagerly may develop a stubborn, hostile attitude which can become a permanent part of his personality. You can be too demanding in your standards of cleanliness. If your child somehow fails to do what you expect, he may develop feelings of inferiority and fear which may last throughout his life.

Bowel Control

A child will gradually gain control of his bowels and bladder with assistance given by the parents. Supply a word or gesture for your child to tell you he wants to go to the toilet. Place him on the toilet chair with his diaper on or off, so that he learns how it feels. If he goes within five minutes, praise him. If he does not, try again the next day. The main thing is to keep a relaxed, easy attitude about the whole thing, giving your child a chance to catch on. Make sure he is comfortable on the chair or toilet seat. A toilet chair with arms is perhaps the best device because when seated on it he is down at his own level and will feel reasonably safe. If he struggles to be off the seat, next time let him stand beside the toilet without removing his diaper. For this child, the goal is to gradually have him accept the idea of the right place at the right time. A seat that fastens on the regular toilet does not feel quite secure to the beginner and flushing the toilet may disturb him at some stages. If flushing bothers your child, do not force him to use the big toilet. Improvise something until he gets over it, or wait until he has left the bathroom to flush the toilet.

Do not be surprised if, after a fairly successful period, the routine suddenly falls to pieces. A trip away, diarrhea, a new person in the household, illness — any change or new set of circumstances — can throw him off the routine. There may be a bit of rebellion as well. Your child is coming to think of going to the toilet as something that is his very own business, because of his eagerness to be on his own and independent of you. To your dismay, he may use his pants or some odd place around the house. This is no time to scold or punish. If you are pleasant and reasonable, he will soon come back to the toilet.

Young children feel quite proud about their body wastes and do not view bowel movements with dislike. The first time your child has a bowel movement in the toilet, you should react with approval. At some point your child will bring you from another room to see his movement, and may dabble in the toilet bowl. Try to understand his experimental frame of mind as you divert him to something else.

Diet should be carefully watched to maintain smooth normal movements. Hard movements can be very painful and this will frighten any young child. He may resist going to the toilet because he does not want to be hurt. The use of suppositories or enemas is unwise unless the doctor prescribes them. A good diet (with fluids and fruit) which helps to keep the mass soft, and plenty of exercise is better than medicines; their use may lead to overconcern about the natural process of elimination.

Bladder Control

A child will not stay dry for as long as two hours until he is one and a half or two, since his bladder is just starting to fill up to near capacity instead of emptying automatically. Boys are slower in gaining control than girls and wide variations can be expected. Training will probably be more effective if you start around eighteen months, because then your child will be able to cooperate. When you find your child dry after a couple of hours, put him on the toilet. His full bladder will soon empty so he will not have to sit for more than a minute or two. Do not expect steady progress. Remember learning comes slowly. Even after he has the idea, there will be many times when he will be so busy playing that he will not notice the signals of a full bladder until it is too late. Then he will come running to tell you he is wet. This should please rather than annoy you because it means he is beginning to realize that this is his responsibility.

Little boys first urinate sitting down and the age a boy learns to stand varies mainly with the contact he has with other males. Little girls may try to urinate this way as well but will soon realize its disadvantages.

Usually children around three gain full control. However some accidents will occur, especially if your child is away from home in unfamiliar surroundings. You might tell him in advance that he will be using a new bathroom or you may take along his toilet seat.

CHAPTER 7

Your Two-Year-Old

Your two-year-old no longer wobbles but he does take plenty of tumbles. He is a "runabout." He can walk upstairs and downstairs holding on to a rail or wall, using both feet on each step. He can walk freely and quickly, run, and will start to ride a tricycle. Your child can build blocks into small towers. He can pull drawers open, and he loves to take things out and put them back again. Washing his face and hands, with much splashing and dabbing, is lots of fun. He likes to undress himself and may do it any time, any place. He is talking in short sentences, delighting in nursery rhymes and simple stories. He generally is keeping dry during the day, but not so likely at night.

By two, your child is busy imitating everyone. He will follow you around as you clean, wash and bake. Sometimes he will be content to watch you and at other times, with great determination, he may try his hand at your activities himself. When father is watering the lawn, your child may try to hold the hose all by himself. On visits to the doctor, he may demand a try at the stethoscope. Whatever your two-year-old is imitating, it is not just play, it is serious learning.

Around two years, your child enters that trying "no" stage. He understands the word "no", but does not always obey it. He is not trying to be stubborn, he is just using and showing his natural independence. During these early years it is wise to let him have as much freedom as possible. When it comes to eating, bathing and dressing, give him advance notice and allow him plenty of time. Hurrying or nagging him only makes matters worse. Be friendly, but firm. Your child is bubbling over with interest and curiosity. A wise mother who uses her child's interest can steer him through the busy days with very few clashes.

In spite of his great display of independence, he will sometimes cling to you, showing how much he needs you and loves you. At bedtime, he just will not stay in bed. He will climb in and out of bed, offering the most ingenious excuses to rejoin the family. Any changes in the household — father going away, a new baby, a visiting relative or moving to a new house, are quite upsetting to your two-year-old. Try to understand a child's reaction to such upheavals.

A two-year-old finds it hard to get along with two parents at one time. He is just learning to react differently to different people. A two-year-old might be quite happy in his mother's presence but become unbearable when his father comes home. He is sure of himself and secure with one parent, but becomes confused and upset by two. If you are casual about the matter and avoid creating a problem, this phase will soon pass.

Chatterbox
The one word sentence of the one-year-old is followed by a grouping of words at two and then many words come

pouring out freely. As young children learn to talk, their vocabulary and knowledge increase many times. They talk constantly, seldom remaining quiet for five minutes at a time. They ask many questions such as "What's that?" due to a real interest in everything around them. All the questions and talk are a natural part of their advancement.

At first, children will speak with cute "baby" phrases. It is best to gradually correct this cute phrasing so that your child will learn the correct words and pronunciation. You can provide experiences to help your child acquire greater knowledge and a wider vocabulary by talking to him, showing and explaining.

Some two-year-olds however, may still be managing comfortably without using words. If such a child is in good health, easy going and friendly, there is no need for concern. Once he needs or desires to talk, he will quickly catch up.

Some experts recommend that if a child is to learn more than one language his parents should start him on the second language in early childhood, between the ages of four and six if possible.

Dawdling

Time means nothing to your young child. A lot of dawdling is actually concentration upon the thing most interesting to him at the moment. Your hungry child may become so fascinated by watching soap bubbles burst while washing his hands that it takes him ages to finish and come to his waiting dinner.

While dressing to go to some eagerly anticipated outing, your youngster may dilly-dally as though he had forgotten the event. He is not purposely wasting time. It is not easy to keep on with the hard work of dressing when everyone around him is demanding his attention. It is the most natural thing in the world to pause and give close scrutiny to a fly walking up the window pane. To your child it is all a part of learning everything about his world.

Although time is very valuable to you, do not start prodding and scolding your youngster or you will be at it for a long time. If your child is being allowed to assume responsibility for his own eating, dressing, going to the toilet and washing, and if he does not feel he is being bossed too much, he will gradually speed up. Dawdling for him will not become a form of resistance. As your child is learning to do things for himself, a little quiet help now and then will tend to cut down some of the irritating slowness.

Dressing Himself

By now, your child will be able to get out of his clothes and may even be trying to put some of his clothes

on. Getting into clothes may be hard for him, so while he is learning, a little help from you will go a long way. You could lay out his clothes so that he knows which is the front, and quietly help with buttons and straps. When your child grows tired of the whole business of dressing he will accept help if it is given quietly rather than if you suddenly take over. He will look upon such help as co-operation rather than as interference.

Tidiness

Putting things away can be fun for your child. He will learn by imitating and cooperating with you. He will become reasonably tidy if there are convenient places for his things. Low hooks by the back door for outdoor clothing, low hooks in his clothes cupboard, plenty of low shelves and boxes in his room, and a few boxes for toys placed throughout the house will help him learn to keep tidy. As your child grows older, he will sometimes put his toys away before going to bed. On other occasions, he may want to leave some superconstruction all over the floor. Even though he will not look at it again and you have to clear it away before you can dust, it is sensible to respect his pride in the project by allowing him to leave it intact for a while. Your understanding in such little things as this helps to establish a relationship which is the real basis of a child's willingness to cooperate.

Good Manners

Your child learns to use good manners by imitating the adults around him, if he is happy and at peace with his family. He will pick up practically all the formalities of "please," "thank you," and "how do you do" with scarcely any prompting from you.

A child may be doing very well with his own family but may find visitors or strangers more than he can take, as they are always putting him in a difficult spot. When visitors arrive, usually the child is brought forward and everyone stares at him. In his embarrassment, he is not likely to behave as his parents would hope. When greeting strangers or visitors, it is much better to leave your child in the background. Keep attention off him for a while. When he feels comfortable, he can enjoy studying the new facts, and with the situation well in hand, he will find his own way to join the gathering.

What your child does or says to make himself part of a group is not as important as the fact that he is ready to be friendly. To be embarrassed frequently by new people can make your child so uncomfortable that he will avoid meeting strangers and grow to dislike new people. On the other hand, if your youngster is allowed to ease himself into the conversation with visitors, he will gradually develop self assurance and a pleasant feeling about such situations. Manners and politeness will come easily to your child when he has a real liking for people.

Playing With Others

At first, young children get along best with one or two friends for a short time under supervision. They like the idea of having someone their own size around, but it will take a longer time before they learn to share things. Your child will go about his own playing, sometimes pausing to watch others, sometimes grabbing a toy or two but mostly concentrating on his own play. He learns as he plays, how to manage his own body, how things work, where they go, what fits into what. Your two-year-old is not capable of prolonged concentration, he will run from one activity to the next. He will be happiest playing alone, as long as a friend or mother is within earshot and he has a variety of things to play with.

Fear

It is quite normal for children to be frightened at times. A sudden loud "bang," an unexpected fall, being lost in a crowd, or the fright of a hallowe'en mask are temporary fears. They usually subside as quickly as they arise, for they can be dispelled by a loving hug and calm reassurance. However, prolonged or intense fears can give trouble unless they are dealt with at an early stage. They can do harm to your child's developing personality. Such fears can result from many situations such as an overly stern father, too rigid toilet training, or harsh disapproval of getting dirty while playing.

Fears can best be prevented in the small child by parents being tolerant and friendly about his progress or lack of it in eating, playing and keeping dry. Your child needs approval for his early efforts. Do not withdraw your love. If you make him feel like a failure, he may develop strong fears.

The child who grows up in surroundings of reasonable security is unlikely to be fearful. The one who receives little praise, who is not encouraged for his attempts to help his parents is kept from building the confidence he needs to develop new skills.

Fears at Bedtime

At bedtime, your two-year-old may prove to be a genius at finding reasons for calling you or getting up again and again. He wants a drink, has to go to the toilet, a little scratch needs immediate attention, now his bed needs straightening up, then he is thirsty again. Being angry, punishing him or locking his door will only make matters worse. It may be that your child is beginning to find it lonesome being separated from you and the family at bedtime. Leaving the bedroom door partially open will help. A little extra comforting and some favourite toys may relieve this feeling of loneliness. His worry needs to be handled sympathetically.

Fear of wetting the bed can make your child afraid to go to sleep for hours. If you disapprove whenever he has an accident, he is bound to be worried. He is afraid he will lose your love if he wets the bed. At two years, his bladder control is not well enough developed to be reliable. Although very tired, he keeps himself awake because he is anxious about wetting in his sleep. He will frequently call that he has to go to the toilet although when he gets there he cannot do anything. Such a child needs to be assured that you love him wet or dry. If this kind of situation seems to be present there should be a general easing of all the pressure on him to do more than he is ready to do.

In some cases, a two-year-old may be afraid at bedtime because his mother has been away in hospital, on a trip or has taken a job. He clings to her and fights sleep so he can make sure she does not go away and leave him while he cannot do anything about it. He is particularly sensitive at this age and deeply upset by any absence of his mother. If you have to go away you must tell him. The person selected to care for him should be warm and friendly. She should have at least a few days while you are around to get acquainted.

When any small child becomes afraid of going to sleep, sitting with him until he falls into a sound sleep is a good way to begin overcoming his fear. It takes time but you can read or sew. The comfort of your nearness will go a long way toward building the security he needs to banish his fears.

CHAPTER 8

Your Three- to Six-Year-Old

At three, your child is no longer a toddler, but an active, noisy, eager "preschooler" enjoying the world around him. He dresses and undresses himself, but needs help with shoe laces and bows. He eats neatly, managing his fork and spoon so well that he can talk and eat at the same time. He runs from activity to activity. He makes a hurried stop at the toilet before rushing out to play.

Your three-year-old imitates your activities in play because he wants to grow up to be like you. He wants to please you and help you. He is easy to get along with. He comes when called. There will be times however, when he has his own ideas about what he wants to do.

Your child is alive with curiosity about the people and things around him. He asks many simple questions such as why, what and how. He is trying to learn about the world around him. He also learns by doing. He enjoys modelling clay, playing in a sandbox and playing house. He uses crayons quite well. Give him large sheets of paper to draw freely. Even though his creations are poorly done by adult standards, they are serious learning for him.

By the third birthday, things should be arranged so that he can do for himself. This may be hard for some parents to do, calling for trust in letting the child learn by trying things out, frequently making mistakes. With parents' guidance, a child can find out that people will listen to him, let him make some decisions. In this way he does not need to fight to get his way. He is beginning to cooperate.

Your child is now playing more with other children. He is beginning to share his possessions and to know the difference between right and wrong. He is beginning to think for himself and develop a conscience. He needs your support as he gains an inner control over his behaviour.

Three-year-olds have a great interest in order and routine. They like to have things done in the same order because then it is predictable. With an established routine they know what comes next and are likely to tell you when you go astray.

Your four-year-old requires your trust, your respect and your acceptance of his conflicting emotions. He will still ask endless questions but will not always listen or wait for the answers. He will boast of accomplishments, exaggerate experiences and confuse fact and fantasy.

Many parents find it easy to go along with their child's "pretend" games. It is best to help your child to tell the truth and acknowledge his mistakes. Subtle shades of truth can be difficult to explain to children. However, time and tactful handling of your child's efforts to achieve honesty and kindness in his dealing with others and himself will help him to live in the world of reality. Until your child no longer appreciates Santa Claus and the Easter Bunny, you may continue to use these imaginary figures. When he is older, let him play Santa Claus and help the Easter Bunny. Your child may have imaginary playmates; these friends are all right unless they remain too long or keep your child from responding to other "real" children.

A four-year-old may resist his mother's authority, but he still wants to be sure that she is around when he needs her. He will probably obey his father more than his mother, because he is growing more and more independent and breaking away from his closeness to her.

At five your child responds to reason, knows right from wrong, and truth from falsehood. He can express his ideas. He likes to go places such as the zoo and on picnics with the whole family. He likes to cut, paste and draw pictures. He prefers playing with other children especially in group projects such as building houses, sand castles and forts.

With his ever increasing knowledge and experience, he comes to understand what he sees on television. You may want to talk with your child about the programs he watches, so that he can begin to relate the content to everyday living. Many families enjoy watching television together, since age differences do not matter as much in watching some television programs as they do in other activities.

Occasionally your five-year-old will really want to work around the house. He will help you with the dishes or the washing. He will help his father with some hammering or painting. He can be quite skilful if given suitable tools and the opportunity to do something. Doing work around the house gives your child that pleasant feeling of importance which comes from contributing towards the family living. It would be best for a while to let a child volunteer help rather than to assign him certain jobs. Later, he will be able to assume some definite responsibilities.

Talking About Sex

Since your child began to talk, he has asked questions from morning until night. With his growing knowledge he tries to find out about everything he is meeting in the world. Around three, his questions show how deeply he is thinking. "What is lightning made of?" "Do animals talk to each other the way we do?" "Where does milk come from?" ... "How?" ... "Why?"

He asks questions about sex just as he asks questions about any other subject. He has been learning about sex from his daily living and now wonders about it. It is important to respond to his questions without making him feel he has asked something he should not have asked. He may stop trying to find out about anything new, if you brush his questions impatiently aside. He will sense if there are some subjects which cannot be talked over with you. By replying to his questions directly you can inspire enough confidence in him that he will come to you for further information rather than getting it from undesirable sources.

You will find his questions easier to handle if you yourself have a healthy attitude about sex, and if you are prepared to answer him briefly but honestly. It may be wise to ask sometimes, "What do you mean?" to get a better idea of what he wants to know.

The loving care you give a child from infancy starts him on the way to being a warm human being. At this time, you continue to build up his love and respect for himself and others by giving him factual information on matters of sex, in a friendly affectionate way.

Your young child is interested in all the parts of his body. You should use the correct names of the parts of his body such as the vagina, penis, as well as bowel movement and urine. If you give him the names of the eyes, nose and ears and not the names of his sex organs he will

soon discover the evasion and begin to regard the sex organs as "different" from the other parts of his body. It is wise to teach your child the differences between boys and girls by taking him to see a baby bathed or changed. If your child is a boy you can tell him that girls do not have a penis but do have a place to urinate. If your child is a girl, give her reassurance that she was not born without something that should have been there. If children are not allowed to satisfy their curiosity about their bodies, they may become confused and worried. Do not be afraid that your child will lack modesty if he is told about sexual organs or if he is allowed to see another small child undressed. Children quickly learn adult habits and want privacy as they grow out of early childhood.

At some time your child will explore and study his body. The only danger in a child handling his genitals is not the actual handling of the genital organs, but the possibility that he may be made to feel guilty about it. Do not interfere with his exploring. It is natural. To interfere will worry him and make him more determined. If he has had a chance to learn of the physical differences between girls and boys, he is unlikely to carry on many further investigations. Some children may check their friends to see what they are like. As a child grows older, genital explorations may have a different meaning. He may discover that friction on or rubbing of the genitals produces a pleasurable sensation (masturbation). This will subside naturally in a normal child because his interests change rapidly. However, a child who handles his sex organs excessively may have some fear or worry; he may need more affection, attention and diversion to other activities. If these do not seem to help you may need professional guidance for him.

When your child starts to ask about where babies come from, it is wise not to volunteer a lot of extra confusing information.

"Where do babies come from?" They come from their mother. Babies grow in a special place inside the mother.

"How do they get out?" They come out by themselves when they are ready to be born. The doctor helps. Babies come out of a special place between the mother's legs.

Let your child raise any point that he wonders about because he has to think about each new piece of information awhile before it occurs to him that he needs to know a little more. Finally, he wonders how the baby gets in the mother. Most children are content to be told that the father must start the baby growing. The most important thing is to tell your child the truth, giving him enough information to answer his immediate question and in language that he can understand.

If you feel that for some reason your child is afraid to ask, you can help him by introducing the topic. Many natural leads can be found, for example, some relative or friend who is obviously going to have a baby, some activity in the animal world, or some indirect remark of the child himself. Where there is generally a friendly free feeling between the family and child, questions will come pouring out.

Bed Wetting

Most children by the age of four have good bladder control and will not wet their beds. Wetting, when it does occur in a child of four or over, is usually at night. Some children at this age however, have not yet learned the "dry habit". Wetting may happen only once during the night or three or four times. Some wet their clothes during the day, usually when excited and busy over their games. If a school-age child wets himself during the day, the most usual time is in the play hours, at recess, during noon hour or in the after-school period. He may not have realized the need to urinate until it was too late to reach a toilet.

If your child does have a wetting problem he needs your understanding help. Often it is not hard to correct if the proper steps are taken. Be sure to talk with your doctor about his bed wetting. There may be a physical or emotional reason. A child who begins bedwetting after being dry may have a different problem than one who has never been dry. Your child may have an emotional problem resulting from such common stresses and fears as a new baby or a move to a new neighbourhood; or the problem may be from a less common stress or worry resulting from family quarrels or expecting too much from him in manners, neatness or immediate obedience. Whatever the cause, professional advice is often necessary because your child's habit is a serious problem for him, as well as an annoyance to you.

To treat the problem, the cause should be determined, if possible, and corrected. Your child should understand that he can be helped. Replace any feeling he has of guilt or shame with self-confidence by encouraging him when he is successful, and letting him feel you are not finding fault with him when he is not.

There are many simple measures and even some devices which may be helpful in correcting this problem. The child's own physician is in the best position to judge which of all those in use will be most helpful in a particular situation.

Fears

All children have fears and worries which, although silly to adults, are very real to them. The preschooler is

mainly afraid of imaginary people and objects. This type of fear is related to a child's confusion as to "who and what cause what." His mind may be occupied with imaginary people, animals which scare him, violence on television, or overheard parts of adult conversations.

The most harmful fear for children is that their parents will cease loving and caring about them. Children can feel safe in the changing world about them only if they feel sure that even if they make mistakes, their father and mother will love them and be ready to help them. There are a lot of difficult and unpleasant things to which your child must adapt himself in order to fit into life as it is today.

Most fears have a grain of truth, enlarged by a great deal of imagination. They can be very hard to correct. Show your child you are in control of the situation to help relieve his fears. When he is afraid, treat him kindly and gently. Most of your child's fears will disappear as he gains experience and knowledge about the world. If he is teased or ashamed, he will learn to hide his fears although still upset by them and the result may be nightmares.

Fears show up in a great variety of ways; some are obvious and others hard to recognize. Under a tension of fears, your child may be afraid of the dark, or afraid in the daytime to be alone in some part of the house. He may have nightmares, he may start wetting his bed; he may suck his thumb, bite his nails or develop some facial twitching. He may be cruel to pets or may not play well with other children.

At bedtime, as soon as your child is alone in the dark, his fears and worries may disturb him. Often his fears will have no shape at all. He does not know what he is afraid of, he is "scared" and cannot go to sleep. Other times, your child's fears will masquerade themselves in some shape or character recently seen in the movies, on television or in a book. Whatever form your child's fears take, he cannot easily be persuaded that there is nothing to be afraid of. Ridicule or stern measures only make things harder for your child to bear. When he is afraid to be alone in the dark with his feelings, he is demonstrating how badly he needs comfort, love and reassurance, not just at bedtime but during the day, too. Praise your child's daily successes in the process of growing up to help him build up his self confidence.

Children are often afraid of what they see and hear. When seeing or hearing of other people's injuries, deformities and troubles they anxiously wonder if such things can happen to them. Discussions of family worries and serious problems in front of children may be very disturbing to them. Any talk of trouble, in or out of the family, is better discussed when your young children are out of hearing.

A very difficult situation for any child is when the two people he loves most, his mother and father, quarrel. The unhappiness which parents suffer at such times cannot be successfully hidden from their child. He is bound to feel and be affected by the discord. At such times it is wise to hug and reassure your child of your love.

Fear of death and questions about dying usually arise between the ages of three and six. When your child asks these anxious questions you should add some reassuring hugs to your answers. When he wants to know what happens when a person dies, there is no substitute for a direct answer. Following your own religious belief, you can, in reassuring words, answer your child's question, being careful to avoid frightening him. Tell him what he can understand — that when people die they do not walk or talk any more. Each child will pursue the subject differently. You are wise to encourage your child's questions about death rather than discourage them with abrupt answers. Never conceal the death of a relative or friend from him. Try to be casual. Some children will not be upset by a death of a friend, relative or animal because they are just beginning to understand the elements of time and do not have an understanding of "forever." Fears of death usually develop in a child who has sensed his parents' feelings of loss and grief at the time of a death. A philosophy about death itself comes as your child lives, gains experiences and develops faith in the design of the universe.

Parents with ambitions for their child to be the tidiest, best mannered, most creative or athletic, are sometimes the cause of fear. They do a great deal of pushing to make their child excel. A child who feels this pressure of living up to an impossible, unnatural standard usually does not show up as his parents desire, but rather shows such symptoms of fear as developing a speech problem, a facial twitch, or nail biting.

Many families walk under the cloud of "what other people will think." Some parents are forever talking and worrying about it. Your fear of some unknown criticism can harm your child's growing confidence in himself. He cannot trust his own judgment if he feels there may be disapproval on every side. If parents cannot free themselves of their own concern for "what will people think?" they can, at least, try not to talk about it and not impose this hampering fear upon their children.

Some children develop fears when something they are especially attached to is broken. They are afraid that they themselves may also get broken. If your child breaks something or if something with special meaning to him is broken, try not to be angry or annoyed about it. Sometimes accidents do happen and there is no point in frightening your child.

Many parents who do not impose punishment or treat their child harshly, feel free to criticize him constantly. They seem to think that, unless they criticize all their child's clumsy efforts, he will not have the urge to improve and grow up properly. Be sure to comment when he does something well. When checking the child's poor behaviour, put it in constructive terms such as "Try to keep the water from going on the floor" or . . . "Can you remember to flush the toilet?"

Many parents hesitate to praise or admire their child for fear of making him conceited. Conceit is usually a "front" put up to conceal a child's lack of self-confidence. Your child needs to feel that you are always standing by, ready to appreciate and enjoy him.

If a child cringes before his parents as a result of harsh or frequent physical punishment, his home is anything but emotionally healthy. His days and nights may be full of fears. Lying and deception often get started when a child tries to protect himself against pain and humiliation.

Telling Lies

Since it is hard for parents to enter into the world of a child, they sometimes deal unwisely with a child's fancies, calling them lies. It takes time and experience before your child can distinguish between real and unreal things.

You can help your child gradually learn to tell the real from the unreal in several ways. Perhaps one day while washing up for lunch he is full of imagination. When he finishes his talk, you can say, "that was wonderful make-believe. Now I'll tell you something I really did this morning." Then you can describe making a batch of cookies and lead him off to lunch. When reading stories to him, point out which stories are "made up" and which are about things that actually happened.

Some children live in more of a fairy-tale atmosphere than others, particularly those who lack playmates. If a child does not have interesting things to do, does not have others to play with, and lacks warm affection from his parents, he may use his daydreams to give him his badly needed companionship. He may even invent a wicked character whom he blames for his bad deeds. To meet your child's imaginative stories, let him know you regard it as a very good story and nothing more by such remarks as "Now, that's a very interesting story. But how did you tear your shirt?" Avoid making him feel you do not trust him.

When your child is around five or six, he may come home with some tall tales or talk big to impress other children. When he does this it is not telling lies to deceive in an adult sense; it is simply that somehow his natural desires to feel important are not being satisfied. He makes up startling stories to get attention. Do not neglect this need for attention any more than you would his need for food.

Adults do not always tell the blunt truth. "Being tactful" is what they call their little "white lies." A mother who may demand strict honesty of her child would not for one moment consider telling Aunt Martha what she really thinks of her new hat. Children, too, have good reasons for trying to cover up. The harsher the handling of children, the more they will be forced to lie in an effort to protect themselves from punishment or criticism—either of which is hard to take.

If you find your child is lying to you, try to understand the reasons for his not telling the truth. The real problem is not the lies, by the "whys." Children retain their basic honesty by the examples you and others set for him. Remember this whenever you have him tell a door-to-door salesman you are not in or make a promise and do not keep it.

Jealousy

Jealousy is one of the strongest emotions of children and adults. It is provoked by any situation, real or imag-

107

inary, where a person feels he has been displaced by another. Jealousy should be avoided or minimized where possible.

Your child may feel jealous when another gets something which he considers to be his. The most common cause of jealousy in a child is the arrival of a new baby. If he knows well ahead of time that a new baby is coming, he can gradually get used to the idea. An only child under six years will find it especially hard to share his mother's love. He cannot realize yet that it is possible for parents to love two or more children all at once. He thinks of love as being something that is limited in quantity, like a bag of candy. If a second or third child gets some, there is less for him.

Whatever you can do to prepare your child for the new baby is good, whether your present one is the first born or one of several children. Preparations should not be started until your child asks about changes in you or if he fails to ask a few weeks before the expected delivery. Any shifting or reshuffling on account of the baby's arrival home, should be done ahead of time. Your older child can help with the arrangements. Talk to him about the new baby as he actually will be, not as a future playmate. Your new baby would be a disappointment as babies are not playmates for quite a while.

When you come home with the new baby, show your love and interest in your older child rather than interesting him in the new baby. Wait until he asks. Do not make him feel he has to love and share the new baby.

Combatting jealousy is where father can step in most effectively if he has built a mutually satisfactory relationship with his older child all along. They can do companionable things together such as checking the furnace, watering the lawn, playing a few games that your child enjoys, or doing a little reading or talking.

At first, you can help your older child by discussing the baby as little as possible in front of him. When friends and relatives come to admire and bring presents to the new baby, your older child can be given a share of the special attention. Possibly he can open the gifts. Thoughtful visitors may often bring a gift for the older child as well.

If he wants to help with the new baby, encourage him. He could help bring in diapers or fold baby's clothes. If at all possible you should spend some time

alone with him. While baby sleeps, you might take your mending out beside his sand pile. Another day, you could read. It helps him to feel he is getting at least a share of you. Parents who are aware of their child's natural feelings when a baby comes can make sure they are showing lots of affection, and giving praise whether he appears jealous or not.

Jealousy in your child may come out in to the open directly, such as his hitting the baby or it may come out indirectly, in unusual behaviour such as his sucking his thumb, stuttering, not eating, not sleeping. He may be just plain mean and, with great thoroughness, mess up the house. Your child may love the baby, but if he is jealous his hugs of affection for it are apt to be violent. Moping, or being obsessed with the baby are two of the most damaging types of jealousy and may require professional advice.

It is natural for you, as parents, to be disturbed at displays of jealousy, but to handle your child's behaviour in a stern manner will confirm his worst fears — he is not loved nor wanted any more. Instead of crossness or rebukes, try to gather your child up in an affectionate hug and tell him you understand how he wishes there were no baby to take your time. Tell him too, that you need him now more than ever. You are helping him to bring his feelings into the open. He will not feel guilty and unhappy. His wonderful parents understand and still love him.

Rivalries

Real or fancied favouratism can upset the family life as your children grow older. In many cases, parents unconsciously provide grounds for the overlooked child's feelings. Mothers and fathers often make unfavourable comparisons. "John was always so careful with his clothes, but just look at you." "Mary was never so mischievous."

110

It is natural for a child to be jealous of admiration or affection shown by his parents to a child outside the family. It shows how dependent and close the relationship is between a child and his parents. For this reason, parents are wise to refrain from giving too much attention to outside children in their own children's presence.

Some competition and rivalry can be useful to him in growing up. He will learn that this is a competitive world where we strive to do things well. He will have to learn to share and get along with others. Your child will not always understand this, he will simply feel jealous at times. If you give all your children plenty of approval and affection, you should not have too many problems. In any normal household, there will be some quarrelling between children. Many quarrels will have nothing to do with rivalry. Some children who are naturally aggressive and full of energy fight as a form of play. As long as each child can stand up for himself, it is better for you to stay out of children's quarrels. Such spats are one way they learn how to get along together. If, in order to prevent actual injury, you have to interfere, it is more effective to distract attention than to lecture. Remain friendly while firmly suggesting compromise. Young children are not endowed with any special or instinctive love for brothers and sisters. Love grows as they enjoy a happy, secure family life together.

"Blowing off Steam"

Sometimes intentionally, sometimes unknowingly, parents teach their children to believe that they are "bad" if they do not always talk "nicely," if they do not always

111

behave "properly". This burden of guilt can be disturbing to even a very young child because he is bound to feel resentment and be angry occasionally. Even the most friendly, tactful parents have to stop a child from doing some of the things he wants very much to do. When you correct or stop him, he may on occasion explode with his disappointment and resentment. He will tell you the kind of old "meanie" he thinks you are. If you are patient, a little blowing off of steam is a good thing. It is when your child has to bottle up his hostile feelings that they hurt him. If he feels "bad" because he has normal feelings, he will become frightened. The most important thing is to reassure your child of your love for him.

Nursery School

Many three and four year olds attend a nursery school or an organized play group for a portion of the day. When your child is ready to be away from you and his familiar surroundings for several hours a day, a school

112

organized to meet the interests and needs of his age can be a wonderful experience. With a small group of other children your child's age, he can learn to get along with others without being the oldest or youngest as may happen in your family or the immediate neighbourhood.

Go to visit the school with your child for an hour or more before his first day. Then go with him the first few days and if he is unhappy and wants to come home, let him. Some children may not be ready for school. If he is ready to stay without you, say good-bye and tell him you will be back. Some children want mother to stay, cry at her departure, and then stop once she is out of sight. They really want both mother and school. For such a child, a firm good-bye may help get him oriented to school.

Television can provide an organized preschool experience for those children who are unable to attend a nursery school. Several programs similar to a nursery school involve the individual child at home in a variety of activities designed to meet his interests.

Getting Ready for School

Your child is facing an exciting adventure when he is old enough to start going to school. He probably has heard about this strange new place from friends and is looking forward to it with eagerness, curiosity and a mixture of many other emotions. It is natural for him to want to do what his playmates do just as he wants to like and be liked by them.

You are actually getting the child ready for school by many of the things you are doing throughout his pre-school years. Some of these are:

1. Be sure your child starts school in good, sound health; have your doctor or local health clinic give him a complete physical examination. (see Chapter I)

2. Give your child the security of your continuing love and affection.

113

3. Help your child develop a healthy attitude towards receiving instructions so that he can fit easily into the learning process of school life.

4. Provide your child with information about the world by answering his questions and pointing out similarities and differences.

5. Help your child gain experience in getting along with children his own age.

6. Teach your child to dress himself and to look after his possessions such as his outdoor clothing.

7. Give your child the experience of getting along without you for several hours a day.

8. Teach your child good safety practices such as crossing the street after looking both ways.

Most parents have mixed feelings of both relief and pride, about sending their child off to an outsider — a teacher. Your child may push aside his dependence of you and try to be on his own, like his other friends in school. The exciting time he has in feeling self-important and independent may, for a time, make him guard his new experiences as quite secret, something very private and precious to him. He may resent your questioning and curiosity and try to keep his new life apart from you.

Your child may have a let-down during his first few weeks in school. Almost all children show signs of strain such as bedwetting, nail biting, eating little or no lunch or breakfast, or crying easily during the first month. More rest is necessary when a child first goes to regular school. If such symptoms do not disappear in a month or so, talk to your child's teacher. Before long your child will want to share with you his school experiences and achievements. He will proudly bring his "work" home and tell you about the songs and games he has learned at school. Meet his pride with yours — praise his efforts with the same enthusiasm he shows for them and keep any criticisms to a minimum. He will move farther and faster with praise than with criticism.

114

CHAPTER 9

Play and Playmates

Through play, a child begins to appreciate his world, to coordinate his muscles, to live with other people and to become a citizen of his country and community. A child learns about himself and how to get along with others. He discovers the importance of self-control and the adjusting of his actions to the interests of a group as a whole. In play with other children a child also learns to fall in with the ideas of others.

A child reveals his thoughts in his play. He acts out what he sees going on around him. He may pretend to be mother at home, father going to work, the doctor or nurse in the hospital, the teacher or postman. Play-acting helps children become more familiar with the world around them. As an observant adult you can learn about yourself and your family from your child's play. Parents often thoughtlessly interrupt their child's play and give little heed to his play materials. The wise adult who observes, accepts and contributes to a child's play development is likely to enjoy a well adjusted child.

Wherever your child is playing, be sure you consider the safety precautions mentioned in Chapter 5.

Playmates

Every child needs playmates about his own age, to compare himself with others, to discover and recognize his own strengths and weaknesses. Playmates who are similar in age and interests learn from each other. It is possible for each child in a group to excel at something and share the satisfaction of being a leader, because children vary from one activity to another in their play.

One-year-olds will amuse themselves happily with a few simple toys. Two-year-olds will play alongside each other more than with each other, they sometimes talk together but seldom share toys. Three, four and five-year-olds play together and learn from each other; they learn

together to lead and to follow, to share, to give and to take. During pre-school years, boys and girls play with each other but with the advent of school they may choose companions of the same sex. Five-year-olds may form quite close friendships. There will be times however, when your child needs time for himself so that he can follow his own interests.

Although it is important that a child plays with children about his own age, some experience with other age groups can be helpful. By playing at times with younger and older children as well as his equals, he will learn a variety of skills and roles, including those of being a follower as well as those of a leader.

If you cannot find playmates your child's age, arrange to give more of your own time to his play activities. When you play with your child, let him take the lead so that he has the opportunity to develop his imagination and self-confidence.

Brothers and sisters cannot be expected to be the best of playmates all the time. They may be too old or too young for each other. Some days they just will not get along together. If your older child has the younger one tagging along because he has to be "looked after", resentment may grow on both sides. A situation often leading to trouble is when a child's possessions get mixed up with his brothers' and sisters'. It is desirable for each of your children to have a place for his toys and books, and this place should not be interfered with by other children.

When quarrelling and fighting do break out, it is wise to let children work out their own solutions. They often understand each other's motives. When parents start refereeing, the quarreling usually increases. However, they may have to interfere at times to prevent physical injury.

Stories

Reading can be a joy for children and parents alike. Your one-year-old will enjoy looking at pictures of famil-iar objects. Your two-year-old will enjoy being read aloud to, especially stories about little children with much repetition of phrases. As your child grows older, his interests will widen. Stories will increase his knowledge and vocabulary. Hearing stories will help him develop an ability to listen and understand. A child who has had some of his own books and who has been read to at home usually starts school better prepared to learn how to read. If you do not wish to buy children's books, you can borrow them from the public library. It is a good idea to take your youngster to help select the books. Be sure to teach your child to care for these books as they are valuable possessions for him and other children.

Your child will love to hear and tell stories. Stories about what you did when you were a child are fascinating to him. He will be interested in what he himself or his playmates or other little children did or might be imagined to do. Often storytelling leads to play acting or simple dramas.

Songs and Music

Listening to music is something that can be enjoyed by the entire family. Your child will like the rhythm of the music. He will express this feeling of rhythm through his body and voice by singing, clapping, skipping, hopping and marching to music. Do not hesitate to sing with your child even if you have "no voice for singing." It is the spirit of the thing rather than the purity of your tone that will spark his interest. Listening to music should be a part of every child's experience.

Parties

All children love a party, especially birthday parties. Looking forward to a party is almost as much fun as having it. Since time can pass slowly for an excited young child it is best not to "talk up" a party too far in advance. It is a good idea to have only one guest for each year of your child's age. Very often small children are happy to crayon or play with their host's new toys instead of playing organized games. Short parties are better than long ones.

Pets

Your child can learn a lot about the world of living things from a family pet. There are several kinds of pets suitable for children, such as a dog, cat or fish. Be sure the pet is healthy and friendly toward young children before it comes into your home. Teach your child how to care for the pet.

Toys

Your young child needs simple toys with which he can play out his own experiences, not a multitude of elaborate, intricate ones. Parents should not give their child an assortment of toys, hoping he will go off and amuse himself, nor should they buy toys in an effort to make up to their child for the things they have neglected. In such situations, the child usually gets too many or too few toys that are not fitted to his particular abilities, often being the kind that he tires of quickly, leaving him bored, or ones so complicated that he cannot cope with them.

Materials that can give the most creative opportunities to children are paints, large brushes, sheets of paper, clay and boxes. Your child will have fun with these materials by himself, with little or no assistance from you. He will want to develop his own ideas . He probably will not produce anything that means much to you but he will be proud of it. Show him that you are proud of it too.

Toys should be appealing and suitable to your child's age and abilities. They should have several uses and stimulate your child to more difficult and complicated activities. They should be durable and safe with no sharp corners or small loose parts. They should be varied for a number of activities and situations, some for quiet time, some for large and fine muscle development and some for creative play.

Your child will enjoy playing with actual household articles such as pots and pans, tablespoons, clothes pegs, a few boards, large nails and a mallet with a large head for easy handling. These kinds of toys give your child a wide range of inexpensive materials with which to be creative and imaginative. Toys do not have to be bought. It is unwise to overload a child with toys such as stuffed animals which do not encourage him to be creative.

Parents can help their child to develop fine motor coordination and eye skills by showing him how to button and unbutton, to trace lines and figures, to string beads or paper, and to fit different sizes and forms inside each other. There are many other things your child can do depending on his particular age and stage of development. Devise some of your own.

In summary, suggested toys are:

For the one-year-old — sturdy rattles, large balls, noisy squeaky toys, push and pull toys, bright picture books with large pictures, toys of graduating sizes, sandbox toys which will not rust, such as a wooden spoon and a plastic pail.

For dramatic play for the two to six-year-old — play dolls and housekeeping equipment, dress-up clothes such as old dresses, shoes and hats, hand puppets, a cash register for playing store, tractors, trucks, trains, boats and planes.

For the large muscle development of the two to six-year-old — large blocks and boxes, a swing, climbing bars, a wagon, a sled, skates, a tricycle, some sturdy garden tools.

For the creative experimental play of the two to six-year-old — paint, chalk, crayons, sand, plasticine, paper, scissors, old magazines for cutting, simple musical instruments and records.

Modelling clay can be made as follows:
4 cups flour, 1 cup salt, water = Mix all together and store in a cool place.

CHAPTER 10

Discipline

Discipline provides a continuous process of learning through which your child develops control over his own behaviour and confidence in himself. This process is based on love and understanding between you and your child. You have to teach your child to be responsible for his own actions by developing his inner controls so that he can live with other people, limit his behaviour and respect authority for his own safety and the safety of others. He will accept the values he knows you accept. You cannot teach him by merely correcting his actions; you will have to live what you want to teach him. Gradually through this process of teaching and limiting, you impart your value about life and living to him. It is up to you, his parents, to help him learn and build a discipline within himself.

Since you will want him to do one thing and your child will want to do another you must make an honest effort to see things from his point of view. There is so much to learn and he takes a long time to learn some things. When we are adults we forget how much practice we have had in doing over and over again, all the things we have learned. Somehow we tend to think that a child has to be told only once before he gets the point. He will gradually give up his childish way of doing things step by step, but never quickly or when pressed for more than he can easily manage.

Children learn better when directions are positive than when they are negative. For example, "See if you can walk around that puddle", rather than "Don't step in the water". With the former method you tell him what to do but with the latter you say only what he is not to do.

It is also a good idea to give him advance notice that something has to be done. If a child has a few minutes to change from one activity to another, he will accept your wishes more readily.

As your child grows, help him develop and learn inner control by letting him take on responsibilities and make decisions for himself. To enable him to take these responsibilities, you have to explain the reasons for any necessary limitations on his behaviour. He will respect the reasons for things and will cooperate more readily if he knows why and how. Remember, it is the day to day examples and steady efforts that help your child learn good discipline.

Punishment

Punishment will rarely be necessary if you, as parents, start right at the beginning to give your child affection and encouragement. It helps if you understand how and when your child learns; if you realize how hard he works at learning, how anxious he is to please and how, if there is love, he wants to grow to be like you. Knowing what to expect, you can relax and let your child grow naturally and happily.

It is unfortunate that some thoughtful parents and adults in charge of children feel that punishment must be applied for a child's own good. They really believe that, without punishment, a child will not keep trying. To a child punishment means simply that his parents are taking away their love. Affection and understanding will help a child learn far more than he will learn through punishment.

Sometimes a parent will unreasonably punish his child's failure to achieve success in a particular direction. Many a father is determined to make his son succeed in some cherished ambition where he himself has failed. His stern disapproval is unlikely to make his son a success. It is wise to be consistent at all times; do not make your child feel you have withdrawn your love. A mother will complain that her two-year-old is "so hard to manage"

124

and she "can do nothing with him." Such complaints indicate that as a mother she feels she must boss her child. When a child is bossed and punished for trying to develop a healthy independence and self-discipline, he has to react somehow. He may fight back by becoming an un-cooperative sullen personality or sit back listlessly and become a timid soul, possibly for the rest of his life.

The time will come when you are confronted with disobedience. What then? First look for the cause — maybe something unusual has upset your child or he is overtired. It is easier to be patient and understanding when you know the cause. You are less likely to act on the spur of the moment.

The moment you do set a limit on your child's behaviour there will probably be conflict. Your child may protest with cries or pouting. He has a right to clamour and protest, but if he becomes annoying to other members of the family, a quiet place such as his room would help him to think it over. These conflicts between your child's impulsiveness and your limits are inevitable and necessary for his growth. The conflict and crying however, should be largely on the issue of respect and consideration for others, particularly you.

Teaching discipline includes your ability to say "no" to a child's unacceptable behaviour and to stick to it, without apology or feeling very uncomfortable. Exercising firmness in some cases will not be easy. You may have to give up your child's love and acceptance for short periods of time.

What about explosions that are bound to happen? Your snapped decision and quick temper will be passed over and soon forgotten if the fundamental attitude of respect and love for your child is there. "Shut that door!" "Stop that racket!" may not be fair from your child's point of view, but they are only natural reactions and need cause you no remorse. They are really only minor points in the main picture of discipline A mild punishment can relieve a child when he wants to shed his guilty feelings. Once he is punished the score is even and he is free.

Withholding treats such as having to miss a favourite TV program, or losing some special privilege are time-tested techniques of punishment that usually bring results. Isolation to some children can be quite severe punishment. No child likes to be separated from his family or social group. The "isolation" treatment can be effective when used with discretion.

Any measure taken should help him learn what he must not do, not to get him to acknowledge that he was bad or that he is ashamed of himself and sorry. Lip service to the notion of being sorry and "I'll never do it again, Mummy" come all to easily. As soon as he is ready to cooperate, give him a hug and let him go. When he tries to control himself, he needs to be helped along. By no means, however, should a child be sent to bed or go without a meal as punishment. These aspects of his health routine are too important to be identified with punishment.

Constant commands and repetitions usually will get you nowhere, they may dull your child's sensitivity to your requests. If he says "Wait'll I finish this," it is much better, where possible, to let him accept this responsibility for control rather than sticking to the clock. Necessary demands however, should be followed through.

Getting your child to do something by means of a reward or bribe rarely gets lasting results. Even if you are successful, you have unwittingly taught him a lesson you will probably regret, namely that doing things means payment. Your child may become a shrewd bargainer. Threats of punishment are equally ineffective. If it is just a threat and he calls your bluff, he has learned your word is not reliable. This practice is a long way from the love and understanding your child needs.

Spanking and slapping are harsh methods of punishment and should rarely be used. These methods, particularly when used regularly, create bitter resentment in a child too small to defend himself. Since he cannot cope with it directly, his resentment is apt to show up in other ways such as bullying his playmates (a kind of "getting back" at you), developing strange fears, cruelty to animals, or shyness. Harsh punishment is likely to make him more disobedient.

CHAPTER 11

Differences in Families

Families and children differ in many ways. In one family, the mother stays at home and in another family the mother works. There are twins in the family across the street and only one child in the house next door. Yet despite these differences, every child learns how to relate to others from the relationships within his particular family. By observing the way his parents feel and act towards each other and toward him, a child is preparing for his own adulthood. If a child feels secure in his family circle, he will grow up with a good attitude toward love and marriage.

Naturally, the best family situation is where both parents share with their child the daily joys of living. However, in spite of our best efforts some troubles are unavoidable; life does not always run smoothly. Many families, for various reasons, have situations which are not ideal, such as the couple who are separating and the fatherless family. Your attitude towards such situations will determine their impact upon your child. When you are aware of these situations you will be better prepared to meet them.

This chapter deals with different family members, outside adults, differences in families and differences in individual children as they relate to your child from one to six.

Fathers

Both boys and girls need the friendship and love of their father. They should spend some time during the day alone with their father to develop and maintain a close relationship with him. Fathers who must travel during the week should try to make up for their absence when they are home.

Little boys will make a serious business of doing the manly things their fathers do. Your child will try to take on father's mannerisms and vocabulary. This is more than play, it is preparation for his own manhood. Sometimes fathers have the idea that they have to work hard at making a man out of their son, that they should get out and teach him to play ball and other athletic games. Sports are great if the game is your child's idea of fun and if he has developed the necessary muscular control. Father's friendly "pointers" may be taken by your child as a criticism. Your child may get worried and upset about such criticism. It is normal for little boys to cry when they are hurt and sometimes cling to mother.

A girl also needs the love and approval of her father. He is the first man in her life. How she gets along with him will help determine how she will get along with the men she meets as she grows up. Her father's approval encourages her to become more feminine.

Grandparents

Youngsters always enjoy in a special way, grandma's lap or grandpa's knee. The attention that grandparents give to their grandchildren is usually less anxious and less concerned with the details of daily living than that given by parents. More than fun, a feeling for the past and for the durability of the family comes from grandparents' stories about "when mother was a little girl . . . " or "when father was a little boy . . . " Your child is learning how to relate to other adults by sharing experiences with his grandparents.

Today more and more grandparents are living on their own, separate from their children and grandchildren. Frequently grandparents who live far away will want to have a long visit with their grandchildren, especially if they seldom see them. The grandparents will want to play with your children, put them to bed and tell them stories. Generally, short visits work best for all three generations. You, as parents, may resent the differences in methods your parents use. Also, grandparents despite themselves, are apt to find the care of little ones too much.

Your Babysitter

A good babysitter is an important consideration to parents. You, as parents, need the opportunity to go out on occasion without your children. You will want to go out knowing your children are protected under the care of a dependable sitter, who will protect your child's health and happiness in any situation which might arise. Check the references of a sitter before hiring her to be sure she is healthy — mentally, socially and physically. Make sure she regards babysitting as a serious job and understands the care of children. Regardless of how often or how long you use a sitter, she must be someone who can be trusted. It is wise to use the same sitter or as few sitters as possible.

A babysitter has three main responsibilities; to keep your child healthy, safe and busy. The day to day care your child receives has much to do with his health. A sitter should be familiar with your child's schedule of sleep, his activities and his diet. She should carry his schedule out as far as possible. A sitter should always know where he is and what he is doing. She must keep your child safe as mentioned in Chapter 5. By knowing how to keep your child happily occupied, a sitter can prevent most disciplinary problems. She will find it helpful to have some games and tricks handy which will appeal to all ages of children.

Many teenagers do babysitting. Sitting gives the teenager an opportunity to develop high standards of service and responsibility applicable to future full time employment. It also helps prepare them for parenthood and other areas of family life. Acquaint the teenager or any sitter with your household and your way of doing things. As children grow older they are likely to tell a sitter "mother lets me do that." When a sitter is acquainted with your ways she will be able to distinguish fact from your child's understandable desire to try her out.

Provide your sitter with written instructions on the care of your child, where you and relatives or close friends could be reached. Also leave the number of the family doctor, the fire department, police department, taxi  company and the hospital. A sitter should have other information. How do you regulate the heat? What are your ideas on snacks and watching TV? Do you permit her to have friends in or use the telephone for long conversations? Be sure to call if you are delayed from returning at the expected time.

Both your child and the sitter will be more comfortable when they know each other. Before you leave your child with a new sitter ask the sitter to come to meet your child so that they can become friends. Never leave your child with a new strange sitter he has not met, especially when he is asleep. If he awoke to a stranger in your absence he might become fearful. This could lead to many bedtime problems. Your child may lie awake at night, cry often, or refuse to go to bed until he is completely reassured that he can trust you again. You could tell an older child before he goes to bed that you are going out and the sitter is coming. He will be able to go to bed and remember that you have gone out.

The Only Child

Bringing up an only child does not present a unique problem since every firstborn in any family is an "only" child. All parents have the fun of a small family for at least part of their parenthood. Spared the efforts of meeting the needs of many children, with an only child you can concentrate on following through the interests and activities that will enrich your child's life.

An only child will lack some normal influences which are part of the development of a healthy, well-adjusted adult. One factor is the support which comes from things as shared secrets, loyalties and experiences that several children in the same family can give to one another. Your only child will miss the world of make-believe enriched by play with brothers and sisters, especially if he spends too much time solely in the company of adults. You can help your child gain this companionship by helping him to find playmates his own age. This will help him to learn to get along with others. A nursery school could supply the playmates for your child and the experiences necessary for good social growth. In any event, you should be sure you give your child your warm support and understanding.

An only child can be over-emphasized as the centre of attention. The greatest concern of many parents of an only child is the feeling that he will be lonely. It is only natural that some parents try to make up for the possible "loneliness" by extra attentions and care, unfortunately to the point of over-indulgence. The youngster is constantly in the spotlight. It becomes his measuring stick for love. The more attention he gets the more he figures daddy and mommy love him. Therefore, he reasons, by demanding more attention he will get more love. Soon parents are being run ragged by trying to feed an appetite that simply cannot be satisfied. The result is truly the "spoiled child." A child is not spoiled by love. Love is the only sound basis for your child's healthy growth. It gives him self-respect and confidence, and establishes firmly the all-important feeling of security. What can make your child spoiled and demanding is the smothering over-protective kind of love which cuts him off from learning the things he has to learn. Overprotection and overindulgence give him a distorted view of the world in which he is growing up.

The Gifted Child

Every child needs his parents' help and understanding so that he can grow up to make the best of himself — his best, not his parents' or teacher's best. Sometimes exceptionally brilliant or talented children never really get this chance. Without realizing it, unsuspecting parents thwart their child's curiosity, drive and exceptional talents, so that he grows up to be a mediocre unhappy adult. Many brilliant children go unnoticed because their parents do not know what to expect. They can be overlooked at school too, since very bright children are apt to find their work too simple, become bored and do not complete it.

To determine if your child is gifted, there are several things to watch for. An exceptionally intelligent child usually starts to talk early. If he says "Mama" or "Daddy" before a year and talks in sentences before he is two, he may be unusually bright. The number of words he uses may give an indication of his brightness, however a lot depends on his home environment and his desire to talk. By five, sometimes younger, very bright children often have taught themselves to read. They have a never-ending curiosity and appetite for knowledge. They are extremely quick learners and pick up explanations the first time without having to have them repeated. Good at solving problems, their memories, too, are usually very good.

134

There are children with extraordinary artistic or other talents. They are harder to spot. Just because your child loves to paint, draw, or play on a piano does not mean he will become a Picasso or Mozart. Most young children go through this stage, but the particularly gifted ones show a more noticeable and constructive interest which persists. They become completely immersed in their special pursuits, and their energy and drive seem inexhaustible. The specially talented and artistic child also has a remarkable sense of colour, touch, sound or smell. He is likely to show outstanding originality, perseverance and powers of concentration.

Some of the myths about gifted children just are not true and may need clarification. Bright children tend to be superior in size, strength, muscle-control and general health. The idea that they are physically weak, unsocial, and bookish is untrue. Gifted children tend to be superior in more than one area of performance.

Since the gifted child is usually curious and quick thinking, he needs even more opportunities than his playmates to satisfy his creative demands. A nursery school experience can be very valuable to him. He could be taken to the public library at a young age. Father could take him on Saturday or Sunday outings to such places as the museum, fire and police station, or airport. Your child will develop his special talents for a full and satisfying future if he is given the chance to explore, experiment, ask questions and learn.

No matter how gifted your child may be, always remember that he is still a child. People are apt to think of him as older and perhaps more mature. He needs to be allowed to feel that he can act as a child. He has the same need to be liked and wanted, the same need for praise and recognition. Your warmth, understanding, acceptance and encouragement will help him to make the most of his special talents.

The Slow Learner

The child who is a slow learner takes a little longer than other children to grow and develop. Some slow learners are born with less than an average degree of intelligence. Their intelligence develops at a steady but slow rate. In a few cases a child's slowness results from a disease, injury, lack of encouragement, or mistaken parental handling. When a child takes a long time to learn how to dress himself, it maybe an early sign of slowness. A child who has a hard time learning safety habits due to a confusion as to cause and effect may be a slow learner; for example, a slow learner may be hurt several times before he learns that something hot will burn him. If you suspect that your child is a slow learner, consult the doctor who may refer you to a specialist who will examine him and measure his development in several ways.

Many of the behaviour problems of a slow learner have nothing to do with low intelligence but are caused by parents who may not understand his special need for patience and encouragement. A serious mistake is made by parents who ignore their child's problem and try to prove to themselves and others that he is just as advanced as the next child by attempting to teach him skills and manners before he is ready. Constant pressure will damage any child's growing self confidence, besides making him balky and irritable. Never give a slow learner the feeling that he is hopeless in not meeting your expectations. A slow child has the same needs as all children and requires your love, support and understanding.

A slow learner must be given opportunities to express himself, to learn and to be creative. Provide your child with play materials such as crayons, paper, clay and water, that will allow him to express his ideas and feelings in a physical way. Take him to see different places that would interest him such as the park, train station and zoo. He may want to go back several times. The slow child must be allowed to develop at his own rate of advancement in such things as eating and toilet habits. By watching your child play and communicate with others, you can learn his particular patterns and needs. Then you can help and guide him to develop to his full potential at his own rate.

Moving

Today nearly every family moves at some time, maybe only a few miles away or possibly a long distance. Your one to three year old may not be as upset by a move as your four or five year old who has to leave his friends and teacher. As long as your young child stays with you, things seem to right themselves when he sees his familiar bed and toys again. For this reason, it is wise to take along any shabby or outgrown objects that are important to him. He would be upset to see his treasures thrown on the garbage pile with you busy and preoccupied in the process of upheaval. Some children become upset at the time of a move and others show signs of upset several weeks later. While you will be eager to get at the curtains and setting up of your new house you should try to devote as much time as possible to your young child. In the long run you will save both time and emotional energy.

Twins

Twins should always be considered as two distinct individuals. If you have twins in your family, take care to

be equally affectionate with both children. Your young-sters should be encouraged to think and act independent-ly of each other and to dress differently if they want. Thoughtful parents will al-ways refer to their children by name rather than as "the twins." If, within your own home, they are not forever being given half status, if they are not always being compared one with the other, and if their possible differ-ences in growth, weight, skills and personality are accepted

137

as being perfectly natural, they will stand up better under the sometimes not-too-wise comments of outsiders.

Adoption

Adopted children grow up in two types of families. In the first type of family either the adopted child is the only child or all the children are adopted. In the second type of family there are both natural and adopted children. This section on adoption has been included for those parents who already have an adopted child or who may be considering adopting a child between the ages of one and six.

Parents who have already adopted a child do not need to be told the difficulty of trying to reach a decision to adopt, and of the importance of trying to assess their true motives for making an adoption. To adopt a healthy infant, once the decision has been made, is not difficult. But to adopt an older child who has already been placed in several foster homes, or a handicapped child, or a child of a different race may present problems of adjustment on the part of both parents and child.

Those with experience in the field of adoption recommend that adoptions be undertaken with the help of a provincially approved adoption society or agency — not privately. Approved agencies and societies provide guidance and assistance to prospective parents by helping them to reach a sensible decision about adoption and by assisting them in many ways after adoption. These agencies are experienced in dealing with the legal side of adoption. They have access to more children and are responsible for protecting the best interests of both the parents and the child, which is not always true in private adoptions.

The health supervision of the adopted child will be the same as that of any other child. It should be based upon a careful medical assessment of the child before adoption including the use of a specialist's consultation, if necessary. The information from this assessment should be available to you together with any history of previous illness in the child, and any familial illness, that is, illness which tends to occur in several family members, such as allergy. With this information you and the family doctor together can provide the best care.

Like all children, an adopted child needs constant love and care. Depending upon his experiences prior to adoption he may require special consideration. An adopted child may fear that he will either lose your affection or be rejected. This fear may cause him to respond in an exaggerated way to punishment or correction. Even though he may be well behaved when first placed in your home, his behaviour is likely to get progressively worse as he settles into his new surroundings. This behaviour will occur when an adopted child expresses his true feelings and tries to test you out. Lying, stealing and destructive behaviour is not unusual for an older adopted child. Once an older child is certain that his behaviour will not cause you to reject him and that he can really trust you, this behaviour will stop. However, the older a child is when adopted, the longer the settling in period will take. Parents of infants and younger children are often over anxious and may try to protect their adopted child from even the smallest unpleasant event. They do not want to discipline or be firm for fear their new child will turn away from them.

All children as they grow up have great curiosity about where they came from and may have fantasies of being foundlings. These fantasies will continue in adopted children throughout life since they do not know their natural parents. Thus it is most important that even though adoptive parents have great trouble in discussing with their children what went on before adoption, they must do this. An adopted child should grow up with the knowledge that he is adopted and he must be told more than once. Since the most curious and anxious child may be the one who asks no questions, you must raise the subject.

Advice from the agency, the doctor, and other couples with adopted children may help to prevent some problems. You should not be too proud to seek help early.

When you bring an adopted child into a new home where there are natural children, a period of adjustment will again be necessary, just like that following the birth of a new baby. The reactions to the adopted child will depend upon the ages of the children involved and upon your attitudes and true motives for adoption.

Some adoptive parents try to persuade themselves that they are no different from parents with natural children; however, there are many differences and it is healthier to acknowledge them. One important difference is the fact that the adoptive mother has not carried this child as a part of her for the duration of pregnancy, nor has she experienced the excitement and anxiety of pregnancy and childbirth. Another difference is that parents of an adopted child have been spared a grossly malformed child and have been able to exercise some selection of the type and usually the sex of their child. In addition, an adoptive parent can return the child to the agency during the probationary period, if too many problems arise. The tendency of parents to blame a child for any problems which arise is not confined only to adoptive parents, but is more likely to occur to them and must be avoided. Acknowledging these differences will help you to concentrate on the great opportunity you have to raise a child and give him the opportunity to develop to his full potential.

The Working Mother

There is no doubt among child health authorities that mothers should be with their children in the early months of life. However, today many women must leave their homes to report to an office, school, hospital, factory, laboratory or store. There are many reasons why women go out to work; for one woman it is essential to her family's budget, to another, work outside the home may be essential to her concept of herself as a contributor to society.

Whatever her reason for working, such a mother needs to consider carefully where and by whom her child is cared for. The person to care for a child must be in good health. Whether in the child's own home or outside the home the surroundings must be safe, clean and in compliance with the regulations set up in your area. Some municipalities have organized facilities for day care services and other communities have recognized the need for such facilities. There are also privately operated foster homes. Foster home day care facilities are few and the needs are far from being adequately met. Your child should be cared for in a day care centre where his individual needs can be met. When he is three or over, a nursery school could provide him with the opportunity to learn with a small group of other children.

You will, of course, want to spend some carefree time on a regular basis with your child after work and on weekends. It may be hard not to feel anxious if your child's love appears to shift between you and your substitute. If you have a happy relationship with your child and he is sure of your love for him, he is more likely to make a good adjustment to other surroundings or people.

The Fatherless Home

If the father has been absent for a long time or dies, the mother is faced with the task of making the family

life as normal as possible. You should not slavishly dedicate all your life to your family. Contact with your friends and some outside interests will help you to maintain a more wholesome attitude with the children. If a father has to be absent from home for long periods, he should keep in close touch with his growing family. Letters should be exchanged frequently so that both your children and their father can keep acquainted with each other. After your children are two years old, whether boy or girl, they should have some regular companionship with men. Perhaps frequent visits with relatives could be arranged so that your children can have some rough and tumble masculine play, as well as a little praise and encouragement from a man's point of view. It is a good thing for your children to go to a playground, camp or school where there are men instructors.

The Motherless Home

If, for any reason, a father has to care for his children alone, remaining in the family home and getting some competent person who is kindly and patient to take care of his children is better for the children than breaking up the family. Your love and approval is especially necessary for your motherless children. It is important that you spend some time with them every day, perhaps at bedtime, when you could tell them a story and tuck them in bed yourself.

Separation

Parents who are considering separation should discuss their problems with a doctor, clergyman or social agency. Sometimes an outsider can help find the cause and possible correction of the problems. Continual quarreling or lack of affection and respect between parents can be very damaging to a young child.

As soon as you have made a definite decision to separate tell your child. He will be disturbed by the family crisis though he may not talk about it. Try not to put the blame anywhere, though it is very difficult, when parents are angry and hurt not to blame each other. You should each reassure your child that you still love him even though you no longer love each other. He may be afraid that he somehow caused your separation. Explain to him that you just cannot manage to get along together and you both feel it would be better to live apart.

PART III

Potential Behaviour Problems

CHAPTER 12

Temper Tantrums

Parents are often surprised when their "little angel" begins to have temper tantrums. Around two years of age, when he has learned to walk and talk, temper tantrums can be common. Even children who are usually placid will have an occasional angry outburst.

Your child at two is old enough to make his wishes clearly known. He demands his right to explore the world now that he can walk and make a few decisions for himself. While he is a baby we expect him to behave as such, but when he begins to walk and talk he is suddenly expected to have self control. However, the "stops" and "goes" of his emotions are not yet easy for him to respond to.

Anger and resistance are the natural reactions of your child to "stop" signs. It is important that you limit your controls over your child to the most necessary ones and refrain from restricting him excessively, perhaps in order to suit the wishes of older members of the family.

Preventing temper tantrums is far better than having to handle them. Hunger and fatigue make outbursts more likely to happen so it is important that your child is getting enough sleep and having his meals on time. See that his learning opportunities are suited to his age level, that he has access to play materials suited to his development and that he has the companionship of other children his own age. Also set a good example by controlling your own anger.

When your child does resist dressing, eating, or giving up some treasured object, two courses are open to you. One is to hold fast to your determination, thus creating even stronger resistance in him. The other way is to respect his resistance, to see the situation from his eyes and to try to appreciate and support his effort to "do it myself."

In the midst of a temper tantrum, it is far better to take your child off to some quiet place with new objects of interest, and to stay close by. Let the storm pass before you talk to him. Remain calm yourself. Do not try to reason with him at that moment. Do not go away and leave him. Punishment will not help him.

The early temper spells disappear for a period of time, but usually reappear in bold fashion during the four and five-year-old period. The temper tantrums of your child, four, five, and six years of age can be most disturbing, causing you to wonder if your methods have been faulty and if you have a "problem child" on your hands. The new outbursts are indications of a new phase in development and are not a "back track." In this period of outbursts parents tend to become exasperated and they sometimes put a more rigid control into force. "Surely by four and a half he should be able to put away his toys," a mother says. In fact, his new laziness, resistance, and boldness stem from a hundred new interests and abilities that he has just developed. From his point of view there is not time to pick up his toys. He does not have enough patience to dress himself. He needs his energy to explore these new interests.

If his temper tantrum causes an outburst on your part, it will only increase his opposition. Give him as much attention as you can during the day; read to him, talk to him and spend time with him. You can help him to become more responsible and to take on some responsibilities voluntarily. When it is obvious that he is trying to make you give in to his wishes by a display of temper simply wait until the outburst is over. When he has calmed down firmly insist that he carry out whatever he must do. Do not worry if he yells, "I hate you!" He will get over this habit of talking back. He will learn to master his tongue since he will still want your respect. It is possible for him to love and hate at the same time and it is better that he be allowed to express his hate.

The Sullen Child

If discipline is too repressive and if not enough love is given to a child he may become afraid to show even

mild anger, and develop an unfriendly, unsociable or moody manner. This type of behaviour is often overlooked because the child is so quiet. He may not speak for hours if he has been denied something or he may mope alone in a corner. All this is highly undesirable, if a child is to grow up to be mentally healthy and happy and to get along with others. A sullen child may get into trouble in school because he has not learned to accept authority. An understanding teacher may be able to help him. A sullen child especially needs love, for it is only on this basis that he can accept discipline. To meet his opposition with force merely aggravates the situation and will not correct it.

CHAPTER 13

Nervous Habits

The expression "a nervous child' 'is often used by people to mean different things. Some think of a bed wetter or a thumb sucker; others think of a nail biter or a child with twitching habits. Still others picture an overactive, easily excited child or a thin, whining youngster who tires easily.

There are several reasons why a child is easily excited or quickly tired. The trouble is not usually due to a disease or a defect in the nervous system. For one child, a physical condition such as a lack of proper food or a chronic fatigue may be the cause. For another child, the trouble may be due to fears or worries which are building tension inside him. Your child's fears and worries — many of which he is unaware of — may seem foolish to you, but are very real to him. The fear of not being loved by you is probably the most common. If you are expecting him to behave with grownup manners, or if you are using too many "don'ts," he may feel insecure and unsure of your love.

Arrange a medical examination if your child is easily excited or quickly tired. The doctor may suggest taking your child to a child guidance clinic or a mental health clinic, where specialists on children's behaviour are available. Your provincial health department can inform you where such clinics exist. In any case, easing up on your discipline and not expecting too much of your child will often help greatly.

Thumb Sucking

Sucking is one of the first things a child does. It is natural. Many children cling to the thumb sucking habit after the first year because it is comforting and satisfying to them.

You seldom need to be concerned about thumbsucking in a young child of preschool age; it is very common for two and three year olds. Many children this age turn to sucking when they are tired, when they are hungry, when they are excited or when they are afraid. Thumbsucking will generally stop altogether as they build new sources of security to help them meet daily stresses and strains.

If your young child is sucking his thumb or fingers so much of the time that it keeps him from enjoying other children and interesting play, or if frequent sucking persists long past the age of four, you will want to find the reason and correct this habit. Perhaps you are keeping your child too quiet for his growing needs. If he is being pressured to keep dry at night he might suck to relieve his inner tension. Boredom can drive your child back to his early pleasurable pastime of thumb sucking. If you restrict him too much in his activities with your "don'ts" or scold him continually, he always has his thumb for comfort.

To prevent or correct excessive thumb sucking, there are several things you can do to assure your child's developing new and different interests. While he is growing and learning so much, he should be feeling, above all, that he belongs to you because you love him, want him around and are proud of the things he does. Be sure that as he grows he has places to play, children to play with and play materials that will encourage a wide variety of activities.

Naggings, ridicule and threats may be harmful and will not help your child overcome the habit of thumb sucking. Mechanical devices such as splints or bandages, as well as bad tasting solutions, may make him understandably angry and resentful. But this reaction for a short period may be the lesser of two evils, if it helps to break the habit. Thumb sucking is seldom a cause of protruding teeth. However, since the correction of protruding teeth is long and costly, it is advisable to consult your dentist if thumb sucking is frequent, prolonged and vigorous, or if it persists up to the cutting of the permanent teeth.

Nail Biting

A child bites his nails to get relief from some pressure or fear which is too strong for him. Twisting a strand of hair or biting the lips are similar actions. Your child will not stop biting his nails because you dislike his habit and tell him he "mustn't"; nor will he stop just because you tie his hands or put bad tasting solutions on his fingers. He cannot stop easily because often he does not even realize he is biting his nails. He just has to do something about the tenseness inside him and nail biting gives him some relief.

The tendency of a child past the age of two to bite and chew things is a common signal of some inner tensions. Nails are tough, insensitive and painless to bite. Once the habit has begun, the rough edges of the nail and the exposed nail bed cause irritation provoking more biting. Direct restraint such as bandages or splints only intensifies the anxiety and strain that are the real basis of the trouble. What causes the uneasiness is often hard to discover since it may have been started weeks or months before. It will take patience and understanding on your part to help your child overcome his habit.

To help a nail biter, you must look for the possible causes in his physical and emotional health. Review your child's eating, sleeping and play habits. A child who is forced to be inactive too long, who does not get enough running, climbing or free play can become tense. Nail biting can show up when too much is being expected of your child and he is worried because he cannot measure up. Build up your child's self-confidence by making him feel that he can do things himself and that when he really needs help you are ready to give it. Show him you are proud of the things he is learning to do for himself. Too much excitement, nagging, punishing or bossing can make him anxious. Play in water at the sink or basin, where you can be with him, may divert his attention and also soften his irritating nails.

If your child persists in nail biting, gain his cooperation by helping him to develop a pride in well-kept nails. Keep assuring him that he is bound to be successful eventually. When he slips back into the habit, try to ignore it so that you will not be constantly checking the child about it. Overcoming this habit may take a long time, perhaps years.

Twitching

Sudden rapid movements that are frequently repeated at more or less regular intervals — such as a blinking of the eyes, a twitching of the face or a turning of the head are called tics or habit spasms. There may be a physical cause, but usually there is an emotional reason. One child may be sensitive and feel anxious in a situation that would not bother another child. Possibly too much is being expected of him, more than he can easily perform, in manners, neatness, or school achievement. If your child has a tic or habit spasm, the doctor should be consulted. There is little point in telling your child to stop the habit as he is hardly aware of it. He does it without any conscious thought.

CHAPTER 14

Late Talking and Stuttering

Learning to talk is not a simple, easy process which a child can suddenly perfect without much effort. When a child really wants or needs to talk, he will usually succeed. The age at which a child will talk and the amount of talking he does depends on the individual child. The quiet, observing child may be so busy watching everything that goes on around him that he may not begin to talk for some time. The sociable, friendly fellow who is interested in people may want to talk early. Older brothers and sisters may help the young child so much that he does not need to talk for quite some time. Twins are apt to be late talkers because each partner spends so much time with the other and they have their own way of communicating. Some children may be late talkers because they do not need to talk, do not want to talk, because of other interests or because they have been made actively resistant to the idea.

When a child is active and interested in getting around — crawling, standing, walking and climbing early — his speech may develop late or be temporarily slowed up until he becomes a more confident walker. It is quite common for walking and talking to develop at different rates in a child.

If a mother is preoccupied and silent when caring for her child, the child may be silent longer because he has missed that warm feeling of spontaneous happiness and his mother's examples of speech. If a child is given everything he needs or wants before he has a chance to ask for it, there is little reason for him to talk early. If the people around him are continually "at him", — coaxing, urging, ordering him to talk before he is ready, showing their displeasure and disappointment when he fails to respond, he may feel uncomfortable and avoid talking. He may build up a dislike and resistance that can be very difficult to break down.

Illness or serious undernourishment can interfere with a child's readiness to talk. Deafness will retard the speech development of a child. Physical defects such as tongue tying very rarely interfere with speech.

Whatever the reason for late talking take an easy-going approach to your child's slowness in talking. Let him set his own pace, watch for signs of his readiness to talk and meet them with encouragement. Do not overdo your enthusiasm.

Help your child by setting easy examples. Use simple, single words in a friendly but not too insistent manner. He will imitate your speech so make it clear and distinct.

Read to your child simple 'few word' books about the things he knows and sees.

Make as many opportunities as you can for your child to be with other children of about his own age where he will have to make his own way. He can learn from their example.

Your child will talk more when he has something he wants to talk about, a picnic or a trip to the beach. Outings such as these provide opportunities for talking and learning.

Above all, do not make your child self-conscious just as he begins to get going nicely, by being too pleased, by focusing too much attention on his efforts or by asking him to show off his successes. You can quickly make him regress by such methods.

When your child does start to talk he will mispronounce many words and only gradually perfect his speech. Some children learn the correct pronunciation sooner than others. For one child mispronunciations suggest a temporary clumsiness in his speech organs; for another child there is a personal emotional reason. Whatever the extent of his mispronunciation, listen to what your child has to say. Make him feel what he says is important. Do not overcorrect or hurry him. It is not advisable to make him repeat a word over and over again in an attempt to make him pronounce it right. Chances are he will go on giving the wrong pronunciation over and over again. You may become exasperated and he may become frustrated. It is very irritating to him to have you try a lot of speech correction while he is trying to tell you something.

Children may cling to childish talk long after they are able to say the words correctly. In most cases it seems a matter of wanting, for one reason or another, to hold on to or go back to the earlier way of talking. "Baby talk" may be prolonged because a child feels that grownups like him that way because it is "cute." A child may return to an early mispronunciation at some later occasion, when he is jealous of a younger brother or sister who is claiming more attention than he. He may feel he is not receiving his share of attention and may consider childish talk the best way of getting it.

Showing your child that you love him without tricks on his part will help him to solve the problem of deliberate childish talk. The child who continues "baby talk" out of laziness should be corrected in a friendly way, encouraged to feel that he can speak well. Remind him how much easier it will be for other children to understand him if he pronounces words the right way.

When the habit of childish talk continues after the fourth year, it should be attended to so that it can be corrected. If your child speaks so poorly that he cannot be understood he will be miserably unhappy. Before he goes to school, expert advice should be sought. Speech therapists are available in a few communities, for example, in hospital centres or in the schools.

There are a small number of children whose mispronunciations are due to physical causes such as the child who is hard of hearing and does not hear certain sounds so leaves them out altogether. If you suspect hearing impairment of any kind, your doctor must be consulted.

Stuttering and Stammering

Stuttering is the speech difficulty that makes a child hesitate and then try repeatedly to get out the sound or word he wants to use. He may repeat the first letter of a word several times, or a whole word. Stammering is the speech difficulty that makes a child unable temporarily to produce any sound at all.

Practically all children stutter or stammer at some time in learning to talk, just as they are unsteady when learning to walk. If no fuss is made on your part, your child is likely to get over this unsteadiness of speech.

Parents who are very aware of correct speech, who have had speech problems themselves, or who have an older child with a speech problem may worry about the halting speech of their young child. They begin to think he is starting to stutter or stammer. Once they have noticed it, they are more aware of it than ever. It probably would have corrected itself naturally, but now it receives everyone's attention. The parents' facial expressions show that they are upset and worried. Their child notices their concern and he becomes self-conscious about his speech. Soon he can barely get the words out for fear he will make a mistake, then his speech does become truly disturbed.

There are other causes of stuttering and stammering as well as the above example. Some children are particularly sensitive to stress and their natural hesitations turn into persistent stuttering. Other children learn to stutter by imitating the bad speech habits of various people. Boys tend to be stutterers more than girls.

You are wise to obtain expert advice early before your child becomes a persistent and pronounced stutterer or stammerer. Ask the doctor about any hestitation in your child's speech when you first are aware of it.

There are several things you can do to prevent your child from becoming a stutterer or stammerer or to help your child who is one already, in addition to the suggestions made for a child who is a late talker.

Let your child speak like a child. Throughout childhood he is learning how to manage and express his ideas and words.

Allow your child to behave like a child. Do not load him down with a large number of rules and restrictions. He may become very tense and unsure of himself.

Try to keep your home reasonably calm and peaceful. Quarrels, noise and confusion would intensify a stutterer's uneasiness.

Give your child a chance to speak without interruption. By listening to him and encouraging him to speak, he will gain self-confidence.

If you are concerned about his speech, ask the doctor to see if he has any hearing defects.

PART IV

The Handicapped Child

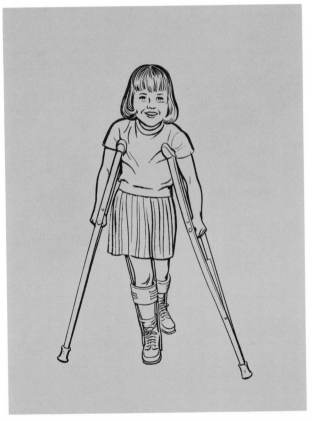

CHAPTER 15

The Handicapped Child

A child who has some handicap, either physical or mental, needs to be treated as much as possible like an ordinary child. He needs to be loved, allowed to develop independence and self-confidence. How he looks upon his handicap will depend upon his parents' attitudes towards it.

As soon as parents are aware of the child's condition, medical advice should be sought and followed. Parents need to try to accept and work within whatever limitations seem to be permanent.

Somehow parents often feel guilty for the child's condition. They worry and fret, trying to hide the child's defect from friends and attempting anything that promises a cure. Such a course hurts the whole family and the child particularly.

The best thing is to try to make life as pleasant as possible for the handicapped child and the rest of the family. Treat him in the same friendly way you do the others. Take him about with you. If he gets around right from the start, the special attention of people won't bother him. To be overprotective or pitying will only further emphasize the condition he must carry through life. Where his difference is minor, a birthmark, missing fingers, toes or such, he should be expected to fit into the family life the same as the other children. Extra concessions or shielding only point up the differences between him and the others. Self-confidence must be encouraged.

Where this problem is more serious — deafness, blindness, major deformities — parents should start as soon as possible to have the child given all the special medical care and training provided by community services for seriously handicapped children. Life can be interesting for them and they can develop into cheerful useful people. These children need the companionship of other children, too.

If your baby is not doing a number of things the average baby is doing, it would be wise to consult a doctor. If it becomes evident that the baby is mentally slower than average, parents face a situation requiring special consideration. If the child is very backward mentally, and perhaps has other disabilities as well, it may be advisable when he is older to have him cared for outside the home, especially if he requires so much care that the mother cannot look after the other children and outside help is not available. However, each such situation should be handled individually. Parents often feel better about having a severely handicapped child cared for away from home when they have assumed the responsibility themselves for a while.

Where the child is only "slower" than average, the family can help him to be a happy, friendly useful person if they accommodate themselves to his slower pace of learning. He needs love and all kinds of encouragement for his slower, less skilful actions. He needs to play with other children. He will be able to get along with them surprisingly well if he has understanding and affection at home. As he develops, he may be able to attend special schools or classes for the retarded and receive training appropriate for his abilities.

If, however, parents cannot accept a child's slower pace and try to force him along just to show he is as bright as the rest, they may reduce his chances of ever being happy or useful. He may become so disturbed he won't be able to develop nearly as well as he is capable.

In a book of this nature, it is not possible to discuss adequately the various problems that many parents face in having a handicapped child. They need to study their own situations and be willing to take whatever means are necessary and possible to meet the needs of the child.

It is obvious that the child should have good medical care integrated with other services and the attention needed for his particular condition. General health needs, including immunizations, hearing, sight, should be assessed often. Dental care and oral hygiene are also important aspects of care.

Regardless of a child's basic limitations the individual's capacity for growth must be appreciated and helped to unfold — with the help of available community resources he should receive assistance to develop to his full capacity, physically, mentally, emotionally and socially.

PART V

The Sick Child

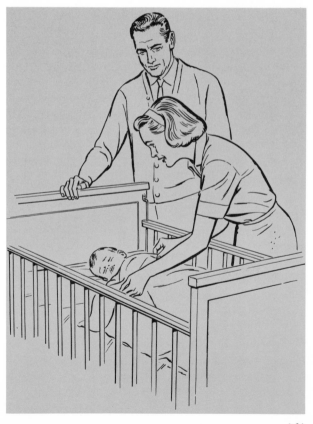

CHAPTER 16

Your Sick Child

Illness is almost a part of growing up. Every child gets sick at some time. There may be a variety of reasons a child becomes ill. Usually he catches an infection from someone. It is wise, however, to remember that a child who is anxious or under strain, such as during a move, is more likely to contract an illness. Most childhood illnesses are not serious and do not last long. Sickness, however, can be serious and can have a special meaning for a child and is sometimes an emotionally upsetting experience. Good care and understanding will do a lot to shorten the duration of a child's illness and prevent emotional upsets.

The onset and signs of illness vary. A small child cannot always tell that he feels ill. The way he acts and the way he looks will show when he is feeling out of sorts. The older child will be able to describe his feelings when questioned, but may not want to admit that he feels sick enough to go to bed.

A sick child is usually fussy and irritable. He often may refuse his food. He may appear pale and tired and if he has a fever, his skin may be hot and dry, his face flushed. His eyes may be watery or glassy in appearance, or he may have a runny nose, a cough, sore throat or a rash. Often a sick child will vomit or have diarrhea. He may complain of a pain in his ear or head, perhaps also a stomach ache.

Parents must learn not to exaggerate signs of illness or panic with every sniffle or pain a child develops. On the other hand, signs of disease must be viewed critically and calmly. What appears to be an ordinary head cold

may prove to be the measles in a day or two, as new symptoms appear. To worry a sick child with too much concern over his illness only results in scaring him and increasing his discomfort. If a child appears very ill, out of proportion to the evident signs of illness, consult the doctor immediately. When certain diseases are prevalent in the community, even in mild epidemic proportions, be aware of them and consider symptoms with suspicion until they are proven otherwise.

In calling the doctor, it will help if you can tell him about the child's symptoms, for example, if he has a fever, is vomiting, or has diarrhea.

There are several things you can do even if a doctor has been called. Keep your child quiet or in bed if he has a fever. Keep him away from other children, as many illnesses are most contagious in the early stages. It is not wise to try to treat a sick child without the doctor's advice; do not give your child any medicine, even a laxative, without advice. Some medicines may even make it difficult for the doctor to determine the nature of the illness.

The relationship between the doctor and your child should be a friendly one. Your child should have confidence in the doctor, a trust and feeling that the doctor can help him to get better. You can build up this trust by telling him how the doctor is always helping people to get better when they are sick. Explain to the child what to expect in the way of treatment and prepare him for the discomfort of examinations or injections. The doctor will advise you what to do. It is important to follow his directions carefully. He will tell you what medicines are necessary, what care to give and the type of diet your child should have. He may suggest you call the local health department or a visiting nurse organization to help you with the care and treatment. A child is best treated at home, however some children must go to the hospital.

Going to Hospital

Parents may question the need for the child to be in hospital but they should not press the doctor to put the child there. Nowadays doctors try to keep children, especially young ones, at home unless there is no alternative.

If the admission to hospital is planned in advance, tell the child old enough to understand, about the hospital and what will happen, including the unpleasant things. Most five and six year olds will understand the necessity for leaving home and, when not acutely ill, will enjoy the new experiences they encounter. For the infant and young child however, it is different. Any separation from mother or a well-known adult is distressing to him.

Talk to your doctor about any points that worry you and plan to make your child's hospital stay pleasant and interesting. Make arrangements to free yourself to spend as much time with him as possible. The younger he is, especially between the ages of about six months to three years, the more important is the presence of the mother. Since hospitals vary in their attitude towards visiting of children, it may be possible to choose one which will permit you to be with your child for as long as you yourself think it is necessary.

When your child is rushed to the hospital in an emergency, little preparation is possible. Stay with him for as long as you can. If you must leave, make sure he understands when you will be back, and be sure to arrive on time. Never pretend you are just going away for a few minutes and then leave him. While it is most distressing to leave a child crying and clinging to you, be cheerful, promise to be back at a certain hour and go. Such crying is more normal than if the child is quiet and withdrawn.

Home Nursing

A sick child, whether at home or in the hospital, requires a great deal of affection from his parents. He must

165

feel secure that they will guide him back to health. Looking after a sick child at home will require planning and possibly outside help but it is good for the child and can be a rewarding experience for parents.

The sick room should be well ventilated and as near to the bathroom and the centre of mother's activities as possible. The furniture should be kept to a minimum. A night table or makeshift bedside table containing the child's personal toilet needs can save many steps.

A sick child may like to be left alone, to be quiet, to rest and sleep. There is no need to disturb him if he is sleeping, unless it is to give special treatment ordered by the doctor. If he cannot sleep, it might help to smooth out the bed sheets, fix his pillow if he has one, give him a sponge bath to reduce the fever, fix the shades so that there is no glare in his eyes and tuck him in a position that relieves his discomfort or pain. He may want you to hold and cuddle him for a little while. It is hard for a small child to understand why he feels uncomfortable.

Regardless of the type of illness, good hygiene practices should be followed by both the sick child and the mother or other adults looking after him. Hands should be carefully washed with soap and water before and after handling the sick child, and the child himself should have his hands washed after going to the toilet and before eating. He should cover his mouth and nose with disposable tissues when he coughs or sneezes and put used tissues in a paper bag attached to his bed. He needs his own towel and wash cloth.

If a child has an infectious disease, even a cold, other children should not be allowed to visit him until the acute stage of the illness is over. If he has a non-infectious disease, he would enjoy short visits from members of the family or friends. These visits should not last too long and should take place after your child has had a rest and before he is tired.

The medicine ordered by the doctor may be liquid, pills or capsules. Some medicines are made up in special preparations for children and are easy to take; other medicines may be less pleasant to take. If a child will not take medicine in the usual way, it may be necessary to disguise it in some food. This should not be continued as it may build up a dislike of the food used. Have a sip of a favourite drink or a teaspoon of a favourite food ready to give if needed right after the medicine. Medicines should be kept away from your child between doses. Be sure you find out when to stop the medication and throw away unused medicines, unless the doctor advises otherwise.

The doctor will tell you what foods your child may have. A really sick child has little or no desire for food. It may be that he is unable to digest foods at this time, and if persuaded to take something, he promptly vomits. Whether he is allowed just liquids, a light diet or his usual diet will depend upon his condition. Offer him small amounts of liquid at frequent intervals, perhaps every hour during waking hours. He will require extra fluids while he has a fever. Catering to your sick child's appetite will not make him a fussy eater if your special catering does not continue after the illness. As your child begins to feel better his appetite will improve but not always as quickly as his general condition.

If you want to measure your child's temperature with a thermometer, you may note that normal temperature as recorded on the thermometer varies between 98° and 100°F, depending on the method used — mouth, rectal, or armpit.

For all methods of taking temperature, first grasp the end of the thermometer opposite the bulb, holding it tightly, shake the mercury down and rotate the glass shaft until the mercury column comes into view well below 99°. To clean any thermometer after use wipe it first with a piece of absorbent cotton moistened with soap and then with a piece of cotton moistened with water. Never put a thermometer in hot water.

Mouth method — Use this method if your child is over three years. Place the thermometer under his tongue and tell him to keep his mouth closed. Caution him not to bite on it. Keep it in place for at least three minutes.

Rectum Method — Use this method if your child is under three or very sick. Place him on his side or hold him in your lap, face down. Grease the bulb of the thermometer with cold cream or petroleum jelly. Gently insert the thermometer into the rectum about one to two inches and hold it for one to two minutes. Always hold your child and the thermometer to avoid sudden movements which might cause injury. The normal rectal temperature, 99.6°, is about one degree higher than the normal mouth temperature. If you have used the rectal method and your child's temperature is 101° or over, contact the doctor.

Armpit Method — Remove enough clothing so that you can slip the thermometer into your child's armpit. Hold him close to you, in order to keep his arm pressed against his side. Leave the thermometer in position for at least five minutes. The temperature registered will be lower taken by this method, but it is satisfactory for most purposes.

A child who has a fever should be kept quiet for about 24 hours after his temperature has returned to normal.

The Behaviour of a Sick Child

A sick child may be bewildered by his illness. He may wonder why he has become sick and what will happen to him. He may not understand the pain, discomfort and treatment he is receiving. His fear of the unknown will increase if he senses that you are nervous and worried about him. Try not to show undue concern in the presence of a sick child.

Many sick children see their sickness as a form of punishment; they associate it with disobedience or misbehaviour. This is partly due to such common warnings as "wear your rubbers or you'll catch cold." Avoid saying anything to make a child feel he is responsible for his illness and avoid talking to others in front of him about "how sick he is — or was." Every effort should be made not to dramatize his illness.

A common reaction of a sick child is to return to more childish behaviour. He "forgets" the skills he has developed and cries easily with very little reason. In many ways a sick child is treated like a younger child. He has

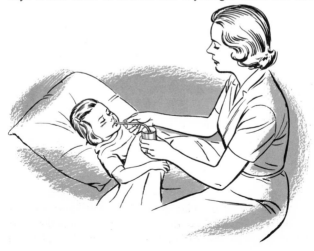

to stay in bed, he eats soft babylike foods and possibly his meals are fed to him. During long illnesses he can lose all interest in his surroundings. He may become completely absorbed in his own body and his physical condition. He may lose interest in other people, except in a demanding way, and make a great fuss over his food and demonstrations of affection. The younger a sick child, the more he is likely to return to thumbsucking, bed wetting or "baby talk."

When the illness is past, the childish behaviour usually disappears. Some children however, get so much satisfaction from all the attention, fuss, new toys and freedom from responsibility when they are sick, that they do not want to give it up. This reluctance is much greater in children who are insecure before their illness, but it also shows up in children who always seemed to be happy and well adjusted.

There is quite a difference between a slight cold, indigestion, or a bad headache that can keep a child indoors for a day, and that of being really sick. A child should not be pampered to the point where illness becomes a treat — more attractive than being up and around. Minor sickness should not be ignored but do not allow a child to use it as a means of avoiding something he may not want to face.

When a child is not seriously ill and is hard to keep in bed because he is lonely, bored or hyperactive, he might be happier dressed or wrapped up in a blanket on a chair in the kitchen or wherever mother is working so that he can keep in touch with her. A change in surroundings may be all that he requires. A steady diet of television is unnecessary.

A convalescent child should be encouraged to amuse himself. While it will be necessary to spend some time with him, reading to him and making plans for pleasant things he can do when he is well, it is also desirable to provide him with play materials so that he can occupy himself much of the time. These materials need to be suited to his age and the degree of activity he is permitted to enjoy. Books may interest him. He may enjoy the visit of some birds at a feeding station attached to his window sill. He might like to make and watch a mobile. He is sure to want crayons, pencil and paper, blunt scissors and magazines or old catalogues to cut up. A bed tray made of a cardboard box can give him a firm surface to make things and play on. Possibly a bag fastened to the bed would help keep his playthings handy.

The longer it takes for a child to return to normal routine and activities the harder it will be for him. He should be encouraged to return gradually to normal activities, to feed himself, get out of bed and put on his clothes. It is easy and satisfying for a child to let himself continue to depend on others, but he must be helped with friendly firmness to get himself back into the regular routine of daily living. This is usually a step by step process. It will take time, for example, for his appetite to return to normal and parents should not force food on their child any time, but especially after an illness.

Similarly, eager attempts to reestablish bowel and bladder control may cause trouble, such as persistent fears, temper tantrums and disobedience. These can be avoided if the child is given a reasonable amount of attention and affection, and his time is well occupied with various interests.

Fatigue is very common after even short periods of play during convalescence. He should have frequent rest and nap intervals. Friends and visitors should be welcomed as soon as the doctor permits. As activities increase, he will spend less time thinking about the illness and his need to be babied will soon disappear.

CHAPTER 17

Some Common Health Complaints

This chapter describes briefly a number of complaints that often arise during childhood.

Fever

Fever is an elevation of the body temperature above the normal level for the individual. There is a variation in temperature with time of day and activity, and unless the measurement is above 99.5°F when taken by mouth or 100.5°F by rectum, it probably should be disregarded. When reporting a child's temperature to the doctor, always state by which method it was measured. Children in the one to six year age group develop fevers rapidly, and these temperatures are often high, 104°F or even 105°F being fairly common. The height of the fever is not a measure of the severity of the illness. In nearly all cases, fever is associated with the infections to which every child is exposed. When the temperature persists for more than 24 hours, or whenever the child seems unusually ill with a temperature, it is wise to keep the child in bed and to advise the physician or a member of the public health team. Fluids should be offered at frequent intervals and a light meal at regular times. When a child has a fever, do not put on extra clothes or wrap him in blankets.

Abdominal Pain

Complaints of abdominal pain are not uncommon in children over the age of three. Under this age, the mother may guess the child has a pain because of the way he acts. It is important to try to distinguish pain associated with illness from that which is not. A child who stops playing suddenly, bends over, or lies down and goes pale and holds his stomach is ill and needs medical attention. The child who in passing, cheerfully says his tummy hurts and continues to play can be watched for further signs. In the younger child, abdominal pain may accompany a throat infection and most children with diarrhea and vomiting complain of cramps. Repeated and persistent vomiting with colicky pain, in the absence of fever and without bowel movements may indicate an obstruction. The pain of early appendicitis is not particularly different from other types of colicky abdominal pain. Since it is very difficult for a parent to find out whether there is actually tenderness present, it is better to consult your doctor. When a child continues to complain of abdominal pain, even if you think there is nothing wrong with him, consult your doctor. There may be no physical reason for the complaint but something else may be upsetting him. Although constipation can cause abdominal pain, it is unwise to use laxatives.

Diarrhea

Diarrhea, or loose, frequent bowel movements, is a sign that a child's intestinal tract is disturbed. There are many reasons for the occurrence of diarrhea including a head cold, a sore throat or other infection, or occasionally the intake of excessive food or spoiled food. A change in the nature of foods a child is eating may also cause diarrhea, for example, changing from strained to whole fruits or cooked to raw fruits and vegetables.

When diarrhea is caused by an infection in the intestinal tract, the child may have a fever and his stools may contain mucus, blood or pus. This can be very serious. A child's body can become dehydrated due to the rapid loss of body fluids. Contact the doctor when your child has severe diarrhea or diarrhea accompanied by vomiting. Keep the child quiet and offer him clear liquids at 10 to 15 minute intervals. Do not use home remedies or drugstore "specials" without the doctor's advice.

The treatment of your child's diarrhea will vary according to the cause. If a child has an easily irritated intestinal tract, he may require extra care when changing foods, or when he has an acute infection.

Vomiting

A child's vomiting may be caused by an illness, for example, an infection in the digestive tract or anywhere in the body. It may be caused by improperly digested food because a child has overeaten when tired or after an excitement; or it may be caused by an emotional problem. Often children who are sensitive to certain foods vomit them back. Vomiting may be the first sign of a common childhood disease. When vomiting is associated with fever, it may indicate the beginning of an acute infection.

If a child is forced to eat, vomiting can become a common ending to many meals. A child may find it a mighty weapon to gain his own way. Vomiting also frequently accompanies the coughing spasms of whooping cough. Sometimes, long after the whooping cough has cleared, the vomiting continues as a habit reflex each time a child coughs or gags.

Vomiting a single time may be of little consequence, especially if a child seems all right otherwise. Repeated vomiting, however, with or without fever, calls for professional attention. Losses of body fluids and nutrients from vomiting may result in dehydration and undernutrition.

After your child has vomited offer him some water. If he vomits again stop even the water. Wait a while and then possibly cool weak tea, without milk but flavoured with a small amount of sugar, offered in teaspoonful doses at 10 to 15 minute intervals may help settle his stomach. You could offer him such things as tea, ginger ale, or cracked ice to hold in his mouth every hour or less if he wants it, once the vomiting has stopped.

Convulsions

A convulsion, which is a twitching and jerking spasm of a group of muscles, or the whole body, accompanied by a loss of consciousness, is a very frightening thing to see in a child. However, convulsions are more common in young children than in adults and may be caused by anything leading to a temperature elevation, such as a first sign of an infectious disease. A convulsion may also occur for reasons which are not understood. Some children are more susceptible to convulsions than others.

Most convulsions only last a few minutes, but a child may injure himself, knocking his head or limbs against hard objects or biting his tongue. Place him on a firm surface, preferably on his side so that he can breathe more easily and will be less likely to choke on vomit or his tongue. Do not try to put a child into a bathtub during a convulsion. If he has a fever, take off his clothes and sponge him with warm water. The air current of an electric fan might help to cool him off. When the convulsion is over put him in bed and call the doctor.

One or two convulsions does not mean that a child has epilepsy, but repeated convulsions without obvious cause over the course of several months are a different matter. The doctor should be called and told the nature and duration of the seizures. The problem is not solved just because the convulsions stop. Only a doctor can determine the underlying cause and prescribe treatment. Do not be fooled into suspecting convulsions in a child who is a breath-holder, given to temper tantrums, or a proficient actor in the game of getting his own way.

Eye Troubles

Throughout childhood, parents should be aware of their child's ability to see, so as to notice any difficulties early. If a child has poor vision, it will limit his experiences. His awkwardness in competition with other children may isolate him from his playmates. Often, unfortunately, it may make him the innocent target of your reprimands and misunderstanding. If a child squints and blinks, holds things close to his eyes to see them, has marginal redness on his eyelids, or seems unusually awkward, these are indications of the need for an eye examination. Therefore, if you notice your child has any of these problems, consult your doctor. Even very young children can be fitted with glasses.

During childhood a foreign body in the eye, inflammation, poor sight, and weak eye muscles resulting in cross-eyes are the common eye problems.

A cinder, a speck of dirt, a small insect or any other foreign matter in your child's eye can cause him a lot of distress. Keep him from rubbing his eye. Wash your hands and look in his eye before you try to remove the foreign object. If, when you look in the eye you see that the speck is on the eyeball do not try to remove it without help. If, on turning back the upper lid, it is on the eyelid, as most specks are, bring his upper lid down over his lower for a moment or two while he looks upward. This will cause tears to wash the speck out. Washing the eye with lukewarm water might help. If this does not work, try to remove it by gently touching the speck with a piece of facial tissue or a small bit of sterile gauze folded over to make a point. Never use a match, toothpick or soiled handkerchief because it is easy to injure seriously the delicate membrane of the eye. If the irritation continues, do not prolong attempts to remove the speck. Get a doctor's help.

When there is an inflammation in your child's eye, it will be accompanied by pain, redness and a discharge. Styes are a common inflammation at the root of an eye lash, very much like a small boil or pimple on the eyelid. A stye is caused by ordinary pus germs that have been rubbed into the eyelid. A warm moist dressing, or frequent soaking of the eye, will relieve the pain and help to localize the infection. One trouble with a stye is that one often leads to another because, when the first one breaks, the germs in the discharge are spread over the rest of the eyelid. To keep the germs from spreading, try to keep your child from rubbing his eye at the time a stye is coming to a head or discharging. Styes which keep re-appearing call for a doctor's attention and a check-up on your child's general health.

Redness of the eyeball itself along with either a watery or pus-like discharge may be contagious, in which case it spreads from one eye to the other and then on to other people. If this condition is neglected scars may develop and injure vision. Check with the doctor about any in-flammation your child develops as well as any crusting of the eyelids, marginal redness or loss of eyelashes.

A marked squint at any age is abnormal. Skilled ad-vice is needed early for a child with cross-eyes to give him the best chance of normal vision.

Ear Troubles

Be aware of your child's hearing ability and if you notice any peculiarities which are suggestive of inability

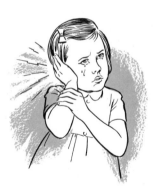

to hear, such as his not re-sponding to loud noises, not attempting to speak, flatness of his voice, unintelligible or hard to understand speech, or not responding to normal levels of voice sounds, you should consult your doctor. During childhood, foreign bodies in the ear, infection, excessive or hardened ear wax, and injury are the ma-jor ear problems.

Many young children seem to delight in pushing small objects into their ears. Beads, peas, pebbles and other objects have to be removed from your child's ear since they may make him deaf, irritate the ear canal and sometimes damage the eardrum. Unless an object is visi-ble and can be taken out by hand let the doctor take care of it. Do not probe near the eardrum.

If your child complains of an earache, call the doctor. He will prescribe some treatment.

The ear is a highly sensitive organ and disorders of even minor importance deserve the attention of the doctor. Safeguard your child's hearing by preventing ear trouble. Leave your child's ear alone. Do not pick at the wax or any foreign bodies which get into the ear. Attend promptly to any infections with discharge from the ear. Many cases of hearing loss in children are a result of repeated colds in the ears, nose and throat. When an infection is not treated early, your child's hearing may be damaged.

Teach your child to blow his nose gently. Violent blowing may help to transmit infection to the ear. Repeated excessive noise, severe blows, or slaps on the ear should be avoided as these can injure the ear.

Nose Troubles

If your child has a nosebleed, calm him, reassure him and have him sit quietly. Squeeze the front of his nose gently between the thumb and index finger to stop the bleeding, holding his head in a normal upright position. If the bleeding continues and if the child has frequent or heavy nosebleeds, seek the doctor's help.

Wheezing

Wheezing may be associated with a number of conditions from a foreign body in the throat or lung to a bronchial infection. In asthma, the wheezing results from a spasm of the bronchial tubes resulting in difficulty in breathing out. Mucous secretions due to the spasms, tend to accumulate in the chest and cause the child to cough. In childhood, asthma is associated with respiratory infections, and is also related to allergies to certain foods, dust and feathers. It is well known that the emotional state of a child will influence the breathing and must be taken into consideration along with the known substances to which he is allergic.

Some cases of asthma are very mild and only with increased activity on the part of the child does it become

a handicap. Other children with asthma have great difficulty in breathing. Wheezing may be worse when the child
lies down. Attacks often occur at night and vary considerably with the season of the year. In the case of a
sudden or severe attack of asthma, reassure the child and
help him to assume a comfortable position to assist his
breathing. Parents of asthmatic children should have on
hand the medicine prescribed by the doctor to treat the
attack. If the asthma is associated with fever, the child
should be kept in bed and cared for accordingly.

Allergies

An allergy is a sensitivity to normally harmless substances such as certain foods, wool, dust, grasses, flowers
or animals. An allergy can appear similar to a cold, an
upset stomach, a skin disease or a number of other disorders. Allergies tend to run in families, with the children
of parents who are asthmatic or hay fever sufferers being
more likely to show allergic tendencies than those children whose parents do not suffer from such conditions.

Allergies occur in children in many different forms
and varying degrees of severity. If your child has an allergy, he should be under the care of a doctor who, by
means of tests, diets and changes in your child's surroundings will try to determine the true nature of the allergy
and so advise on how to relieve it. The more common
childhood allergies are discussed.

Eczema — A skin irritation or rash may be an allergy
such as eczema or it may be caused by contact of the skin
with a substance to which your child is very sensitive, for
example, detergent used for washing clothes. If your child
develops a rash or skin irritation which spreads or recurs,
contact the doctor to have it correctly diagnosed.

Eczema shows up as a red, thickened rough patch on
the skin. It may occur any place on the body, but most
commonly on the cheeks, scalp, in the folds about the
neck, in front of the elbows and behind the knees and

ears. The skin will itch and when scratched ooze and dry forming a crust. The open sores can become infected. Eczema is one of the earliest forms of allergy to show up in a child. Eczema can be caused by certain foods such as wheat, egg, fruit juice or oatmeal, or it can be caused by a sensitivity to woolen fabrics.

Happily, some children recover from eczema but reasonable care is necessary to safeguard against this irritating condition in later life. What a doctor does in studying and treating eczema depends on the individual child, the character and location of the rash, the history of such things as any new food introduced before the rash began, and how the child responds to different forms of treatment.

Hives are itchy, raised spots on the skin, resembling large mosquito bites. They occur on the body extremities and face usually as well defined small bumps. Occasionally they seem to group together, each lump forming a "giant hive." An intense itching is characteristic of hives. Ordinarily they do not last long, often disappearing just as rapidly as they appeared. A few children get hives repeatedly while others get only one or two in their lifetime.

Sometimes hives are caused by a certain food to which your child is sensitive. At other times however, the cause of the hives cannot be determined. A warm soda bath (1 cup of baking soda for a small tub) or a local application of calomine lotion will relieve the itching. In persistent, worrisome cases see the doctor.

Hay Fever is usually caused by the pollens of certain weeds, grasses and trees. The membranes of the nose, tear ducts and eyes react to the pollen, resulting in repeated sneezing due to the irritation and swelling of the membranes of the nose, intense itching and watering of the eyes, and a feeling of stuffiness in the head similar to the common cold. When pollen is the cause, the hay fever is seasonal; otherwise, it follows contact with the substance responsible.

CHAPTER 18

Childhood Diseases

While minor illnesses may be treated by parents, the complicated field of disease must be under the supervision of the doctor and nurse. This chapter describes briefly some of the childhood diseases not as a medical text but rather as a guide for parents in recognizing the signs, judging the severity of the illness, and preventing complications.

They are grouped generally as follows:

Some Infectious Diseases
Diseases Preventable by Current Immunization Programs
Parasitic Diseases

Some Infectious Diseases

Diseases which spread from one person to another are called infectious or communicable diseases. Infectious diseases are caused by tiny organisms called germs. There are two types of these germs: bacteria, which cause diseases such as whooping cough, scarlet fever, pneumonia, tuberculosis, diphtheria and typhoid fever; and viruses which result in the common cold, influenza, chickenpox, measles, mumps, poliomyelitis and others.

Infectious diseases are usually spread from one person to another although sometimes they are transmitted from animals or by food and water. The germs reach a child's body in three different ways:

1. Breathing — through the nose and throat;
2. Eating — through the mouth, stomach and intestinal tract;
3. Contact — through the skin either by directly touching an infected person, indirectly by touching something that an infected person has handled, or through a break in the skin.

Diseases are listed in alphabetical order.

Chicken Pox is one of the mildest of the childhood diseases but it is also one of the most highly contagious. It is spread by droplet infection from the nose and mouth of someone with the disease. A child, if susceptible, will develop chicken pox two or three weeks after he has been exposed to the disease. Mild fever followed by a rash in 24 to 36 hours is the first symptom of the disease, except in those cases where the rash appears first. The chicken pox rash begins with small red spots which appear on the trunk, then on the face and in most cases over the entire body. The spots come out in fresh crops every few hours for two or three days. The rash soon changes to small blisters filled with clear fluid or serum which soon break, forming itchy scabs. Persistent scratching of these scabs may cause scars to form. A soothing lotion prescribed by the doctor or a paste of baking soda and water will help relieve the itching. Trim your child's fingernails to prevent his scratching. A mouthwash will keep the mouth relatively clean and soothing eye baths or drops prescribed by the doctor will take care of any spots on the eyes. Complications other than secondary infections due to scratching and picking the pox are rare. A child with chicken pox should be isolated until nearly all the scabs have disappeared or dried up (about 10 days).

A *Common Cold* may be only a runny nose, or it may be the early symptom of such diseases as the measles or influenza, or it may develop into pneumonia with the spread of infection. Fever, irritability, restlessness and loss of appetite are symptoms that usually accompany a childhood cold. When your child has a cold and a fever, check with the doctor. Congestions in the nose and throat can make breathing more difficult. This can be relieved with extra moisture by placing your child in a small room where a kettle or vaporizer is boiling. Keep the kettle or vaporizer out of your child's reach to prevent burning or scalding. If your child has a fever he should be put in bed, and cared for as suggested under Fever (page 172).

Croup refers to different types of laryngitis (inflammation of the voice box). It is identified by a hoarse, deep weakness of voice, particularly evident when a child cries. It may be caused by a cold, but it sometimes develops when there is no evidence of a cold. The mildest type of croup is the one due to a virus. It is not accompanied by much fever and generally comes on during the night. Your child may have been quite healthy during the day and awake at night with a violent fit of coughing and have difficulty in breathing. The suddenness of the onset and the hoarseness may alarm you and frighten your child. Until you can speak to the doctor you can help your child to breathe warm, moist air by using a kettle or vaporizer. Or you could take him into the bathroom, close the door and turn the hot water on full. Be careful to avoid burning your child from the direct steam and prevent his becoming chilled after he has been exposed

to the steam. If the steam does not work wrap him in a blanket and take him to an open window or door — the cold air should improve his breathing. The doctor will tell you of any specific treatment. One attack of simple croup usually brings on successive attacks for several nights. When the hoarse, deep cough, and partial or complete loss of voice persists the following day and is accompanied by a sore throat and fever, report it to the doctor at once since it indicates a more serious form of croup. Difficulty in breathing, weakness, and exhaustion, are very serious signs.

Influenza is an acute infectious disease characterized by some or all of the following; a sudden onset of fever, aching limbs and back, runny nose, sore throat, and listlessness. There are several types of influenza and repeated attacks are possible. Tell the doctor your child's particular symptoms to be sure of the correct treatment.

Impetigo is a very contagious skin infection and should not be confused with cold sores. It usually occurs on the face, scalp, or chin; but may also be on the hands or any other part of the body. It starts with an itchy blister which oozes and crusts over. Your child can easily infect others or other areas of his own body by spreading germs from the first sore. Teach your child to keep his fingers away from the sores and to wash his hands frequently. See the doctor early as prompt treatment can clear up the infection. If neglected, impetigo will spread rapidly.

Infectious Hepatitis is an infection of the liver which takes two to six weeks to develop after a child is exposed to it. It may be mild with few symptoms or it may be severe accompanied by a fever, headache, abdominal pain, nausea, diarrhea and general weariness. Later the skin may become yellow, the whites of the eyes yellow, the urine dark and the bowel movements claylike. If your child develops any of these symptoms or is exposed to infectious hepatitis isolate him and contact the doctor at once. The doctor may decide to give your child a temporary type of immunity against this disease.

Meningitis is an inflammation of the covering of the brain or spinal cord. A child with meningitis is seriously ill. The symptoms come on suddenly and include a stiff neck, a headache, an intolerance to light, fever and occasionally a convulsion. These symptoms demand the attention of a doctor immediately because the earlier that treatment is started the better is the chance of recovery. Children who have had contact with meningitis may need to be treated to prevent their getting the disease.

Pneumonia is a general name for an infection of the lungs. There are many types of pneumonia depending on the germs causing the infection and the area of the lung involved. Pneumonia may follow an ordinary head cold, measles, whooping cough, or other infections, or the onset may be without warning. Fever, chills, rapid breathing and coughing suggests the possibility of pneumonia. There is no standard treatment and each type of pneumonia may call for a different treatment. Call the doctor and tell him your child's symptoms. Modern drugs can bring about prompt recovery if the treatment is started early. A child with pneumonia may not seem very sick, but the disease can last a long time.

Rabies is a very serious disease. If your child is bitten by an animal, whether it is a family pet or a wild animal, such as a dog, wolf, fox, bat or skunk, he should be seen by the doctor at once for treatment. Although the bite itself may not be a problem, the saliva of the animal will contain germs, possibly including those of rabies. The area of bite should be thoroughly washed with soap and water immediately, before going to the doctor. The animal if possible must be kept under observation for ten days. Rabies will develop during that time if the animal has the disease. You should make sure your own pets are vaccinated against rabies. Teach your child to stay away from unfamiliar animals, whether they are a pet or wild, and to watch for any animal whose behaviour is strange including such characteristics as being unfriendly or overly affectionate, and a tendency to snap at moving objects.

Rheumatic Fever occasionally occurs in preschool children, but mainly occurs in school age children. Rheumatic fever develops as a complication of a streptococcus infection such as a strep throat. The symptoms of rheumatic fever vary. They consist of a recurrent fever or pain and swelling of the larger joints such as the wrist, ankle or knee, or a skin rash. Rheumatic fever tends to recur however mild the first attack. The mildness of the symptoms has little relation to the damage it can cause. The doctor must be consulted if your child has any of these symptoms. Because this illness can only be diagnosed by a doctor following a complete examination, rheumatic fever requires careful treatment. Following the acute stage of the disease the doctor may prescribe regular preventive doses of antibiotics to prevent further attacks. Whatever medication the doctor advises should be taken regularly by your child for the length of time he suggests, which may be months or years.

Scarlet Fever is caused by a streptococcus infection of the throat. It usually begins with a sore throat, vomiting, fever and a headache. A fine red rash develops in a day or two on the body and limbs together with a flushed face. If scarlet fever is treated promptly, it is not a long or serious disease. A child with scarlet fever should be isolated for the first week or longer depending on the doctor's instructions.

A *Sore Throat* (pharyngitis or tonsillitis) should be suspected if your child has trouble swallowing either saliva, fluids or food. Redness and swelling in the throat when associated with fever, loss of appetite and possibly vomiting, indicates an acute throat infection. A sore throat caused by a streptococcus is called a strep throat or if a rash is present, scarlet fever. Whitish spots or patches in the throat area may indicate tonsillitis, strep throat or other infections which are serious and demand accurate diagnosis and specific treatment by the doctor. Tonsils are located between folds of tissue at the back, on each side of the throat. Adenoids are located at the back of the nasal passages and cannot be seen. With each nose and throat infection the tonsils and adenoids are involved. Repeated colds and infections can enlarge both the tonsils and adenoids but their enlargement gradually subsides after the acute illness. Since removing the tonsils and adenoids may make your child more susceptible to certain infections, they are only removed when it is absolutely essential. Do not urge the doctor to remove your child's tonsils or adenoids, he will do it if he thinks it is necessary.

Swollen Glands should be reported to the doctor. The glands which tend to become swollen are small lymph glands dispersed throughout the body. They are nature's second line of defense in fighting infections. Consequently, with nose, throat, ear or mouth infections the glands under the jaw and on either side of the neck may sometimes become inflamed and swollen.

Tuberculosis is much less prevalent to-day, but it has by no means disappeared. In young children it shows up in many different forms. Tuberculosis is spread from one person to another, with little children having less resistance to the disease than older children or adults. It can be passed to a child in infected cow's milk or other dairy products that have not been pasteurized. Tuberculosis is not inherited. When the disease occurs in families it has been spread from one member to another. Tuberculosis usually affects the lungs and the lymph glands at the roots of the lungs, but it may spread in the blood and affect any part of the body. Symptoms common to all

187

types of tuberculosis are loss of weight, failure to gain weight, unexplained fever, paleness and fatigue. Unlike adults a cough is not a common symptom of tuberculosis in children. When exposure is known or even suspected, your child should be examined by the doctor, and followed by regular check-ups by him.

Typhoid Fever is not very common in Canada today, but outbreaks occur every year. It is almost always caught from swimming in or drinking contaminated water. Typhoid fever is characterized by continuing fever, head-ache, listlessness; other features which may occur are rose spots on the abdomen, constipation or diarrhea, and blood in the stool. Illness usually occurs from one to three weeks after exposure. Immunization is advised if a child is exposed to the disease, such as during an epidemic, when travelling to areas where typhoid is prevalent or where sanitary measures are lax. The protection following immunization does not last as long as in the case of some other diseases.

Diseases Preventable by Current Immunization Programs

With immunization, many of the more serious and often fatal contagious diseases can be prevented or their effects lessened so that a child need never suffer serious consequences from them. The following diseases can be prevented by a program of immunization. See Chapter 2 for information on immunization and the preventive programs available.

Whooping Cough (pertussis) starts out like a common cold or cough but after a week the cough becomes spasmodic and the typical "whooping" (gasping for air) develops. Vomiting often accompanies spasms of coughing. The food lost by this type of vomiting must be re-placed once the vomiting has stopped. Between attacks of the coughing, the child may appear quite normal and eat and play as usual. The infection is spread by droplet infection and usually takes about ten days to develop. It is most contagious during the first two weeks, but may remain so for as long as five or six weeks. Immunization against whooping cough is a must for every child as it not only increases resistance to the disease but may lessen the severity of a possible attack. If a child has whooping cough, isolate him until the cough is gone because this serious disease may lead to death, deafness, or other complications.

Poliomyelitis is rare now. It used to occur in epidemics with the peak in the summer and autumn months. It is caused by a virus which infects the spinal cord and results in muscle paralysis of varying degrees. The virus gets into the body through the mouth and nose from contact with infected people, polluted bathing pools and beaches. Moderate fever, headache, occasional vomiting, intestinal upset, drowsiness, and a stiffness or pain in the back of the neck or the back are the usual early symptoms. If your child develops fever with a headache or stiffness of the neck, he should be put in bed and the doctor called at once. Muscle weakness or paralysis may follow in a few cases. It is stressed that polio can be prevented by immunization. Be sure your child is receiving the recommended number of doses.

Diphtheria is a highly infectious, serious disease which can be avoided. Even when a case seems mild, it can leave serious heart and nerve complications. It is caused by germs which lodge in the throat and nose. The first signs are a sore and inflamed throat, feverishness and generalized illness. A child who has received the proper immunization and booster doses on schedule is protected from the disease.

Smallpox does not occur in Canada today, but with rapid movement between countries, opportunities for exposure to the disease may occur. Vaccination gives practically complete protection against this disfiguring disease if it is kept up to date. Smallpox is characterized by a sudden fever, chills, headache and backache followed by a rash which becomes raised and hard. These symptoms develop seven to 16 days after exposure to the disease.

Tetanus (lockjaw) is caused by germs in the soil, dirt or dust which get into the body through a cut or puncture in the skin due to an injury, bite, or severe burn. Tetanus takes anywhere from four to 21 days to develop and its course is marked by a wound infection followed by painful muscular contractions of the jaw and neck muscles, and later the trunk and extremity muscles. Check with the doctor if your child has a deep wound with dirt in it, Tetanus immunization will protect your child from this dangerous disease. Reinforced doses should be continued throughout life.

Measles is characterized by a cough, runny nose, red and watery eyes, and a mounting fever. A child with the measles feels very ill. For the first three or four days there is no rash. The rash first breaks out at the hairline and spreads down in blotches over the face and body, becoming bigger and darker colored. The fever stays high while the rash develops. Measles may be mild or severe with complications of a serious nature. Follow the doctor's advice in caring for your child with measles as it is not as minor a disease as is sometimes thought. It is contagious to others from the very beginning of the cold symptoms. Since immunization is available ask the doctor or local health department where it can be obtained to prevent or at least protect your child from developing the disease if he has been exposed. Isolate your child until the rash fades.

German Measles is generally a mild illness. It is seldom serious in children, but is very contagious. A low fever, sore throat or cold may precede the characteristic small red rash of German measles. The glands behind the ears and at the back of the neck are usually enlarged.

The disease appears about 14 days after contact. Children are immune after one attack. Although there is no specific treatment for German measles it is important to call the doctor to make certain of the diagnosis. He should be isolated until the swelling of the glands has subsided or for about a week. Because of the danger to the unborn baby, a pregnant woman who has been exposed to German measles should contact the doctor at once.

Mumps is an infection of the salivary glands. Although it is usually not serious, occasionally complications may develop. The symptoms appear two to three weeks after contact and include fever, headache, vomiting and a painful swelling of the glands on either one or both sides of the jaw. You should call the doctor if you suspect your child has the mumps to be sure of the diagnosis and the suitable treatment since mumps and swollen glands are often confused. If your child has the mumps he should be isolated until the swelling has gone down. If, after he has started to recover, he feels sick again with a headache, fever or vomiting, call the doctor at once. Live virus vaccine may be used.

Parasitic Diseases

A parasite is a plant or animal which lives in or upon another living thing. Parasitic diseases are caused by parasites which live upon or inside humans. Parasitic diseases are common in young children, and although they are easily recognized, their diagnosis and treatment should be left to the doctor. When one member of the family has a parasitic disease, every member may need examinations to determine whether they also have the infection.

Lice are small animals which attach themselves and their eggs, called nits, to the hair or skin and cause irritation. When your child scratches, it will cause further irritation. The doctor can prescribe a treatment. Be sure to place the medication out of your child's reach when you are not using it. Keep your child and his clothing and bedding clean to avoid the spread or reinfection by the lice. If one person in the family is infected with lice, all the members of the family should be examined and treated, if necessary, at the same time. Also watch for infected playmates and encourage them to be treated.

Scabies (itch) is caused by a small parasite, the female of which burrows into the unbroken skin to deposit her eggs. Scabies occurs most frequently on the palms of the hands, between the fingers, and on the inner surface of the arms, but sometimes may be found on the rest of the body. The itching is most noticed at night when your child is in bed and warm. Infection from germs may occur when your child scratches the spots. The doctor will prescribe a suitable treatment which may have to be repeated in two to three weeks' time. Bedclothes and linen should be sterilized by boiling or ironing with a hot iron if scabies is present. The child's clothing should be kept separate to prevent spread of the infection.

Ringworm is caused by a fungus which attacks the areas of the body which have hairs on them, particularly the scalp. It causes ring-shaped patches which are inflamed at the edges and have a dead or healed part in the centre from which the hair has broken off. Ringworm starts as small red spots and then spreads, causing itching and tenderness in the large infected sores. Ringworm is contagious. If it is decided to treat the child, the whole family will be required to take the medical treatment as well.

Pinworms are small, white threadlike worms about half an inch long which live in the intestinal tract of humans, mostly children. These worms cause itching around the rectum and the child may seem nervous from having lost sleep. Contrary to popular belief, grinding the teeth and picking the nose are not symptoms of worms. If your child itches around the rectal area, the stool and this area should be examined for any signs of worms.

You are more likely to spot these worms around the rectal area at night. The doctor should be notified if worms are found and he will prescribe "worm medicine" which will kill the worms without harming your child. Other members of the family also need treatment. Cleanliness is required to prevent reinfection and the spreading of pinworms to others by means of the eggs which are deposited on the skin outside the rectum. Your child's hands should be kept clean and his fingernails kept short. You should teach him to keep his hands from his mouth. Cotton gloves worn at night may prevent him from scratching and spreading the infection.

Roundworms are whitish, smooth and about the same size as an ordinary earthworm. It is easy to recognize the roundworms in your child's stool immediately following a bowel movement. These require prompt treatment as the eggs are deposited inside the body and may cause problems in other parts of the body as well as in the intestine. Contact your doctor for diagnosis and treatment.

Conclusion

From the foregoing, it is evident that both in illness and in health parents have a vital part to play in their child's growth and development.

Care at home, as well as concern and assistance from the community are essential for a young child's formation into a responsible human being.

Parents and community workers engaged in the promotion of the well-being of children might well ask themselves the question: Are children in this community receiving the attention as recommended?

1. A safe and loving home where family relationships are good.

2. Proper nutrition.

3. Clean, safe habits of personal hygiene, including clean clothes, wholesome play, exercise, and sleep.

4. Regular medical, health and dental supervision, including protection by immunization, from physicians, dentists, and other health personnel.

5. Interest and good example of adults and groups through their practices, the environment, and community resources.

When I was One,
I had just begun.
When I was Two,
I was nearly new.
When I was Three,
I was hardly Me.
When I was Four,
I was not much more.
When I was Five,
I was just alive.
But now I am Six, I'm as clever as clever.
So I think I'll be six now for ever and ever.

(A. A. MILNE, "THE END")